Cooking Up Health, Wellness & Joy!

Judith Toscano
Photography by Judith Toscano and Mitone Cooke
Some illustrations used by permission from Getty Images

Lotus Wellness Cottage
104 Via Avenue
Stuart, VA 24171

Book design by PenworthyLLC

ISBN: 978-0-9972998-0-9

Please remember, this is a guide. When you make any lifestyle change, including what you eat, you need to take into consideration your existing health. If you are pregnant, nursing, taking medication, or have a medical condition, consult your physician before starting any new eating regimen. This publication contains opinions and ideas of this author. It is intended to provide helpful and informative material on the subjects addressed in the publication. It is sold with the understanding that the author and publisher are not engaged in rendering medical, health or any other personal or professional services in the book.

The author and publisher specifically disclaim all responsibility for any liability, loss or risk, personal or otherwise, which is incurred as a consequence, directly or indirectly, of the use and application of any contents of this book.

This book is dedicated to Mother Earth and all her inhabitants.

Always seek the truth and reach beyond your dreams to find your joy.

Table of Contents

COOKING UP HEALTH, WELLNESS & JOY !

COOKING UP HEALTH, WELLNESS & JOY !

COOKING UP HEALTH, WELLNESS & JOY !

Introduction

Maybe you are motivated by lab tests, maybe not. . . . This little cookbook was created to take the fear out of healthy diet choices and surround you with information and joy! To me, this book is a sharing, a way to recognize a new palette of nutritional food choices that perk you up and center you at the same time.

My intention for you is to gain innate wisdom, an awareness of the healthy choices you make and a knowing about what works for you.

Remember a time in your life when you felt great? Here is a way to get it back!

Here are some of the major life changes you can expect:

A better-looking, better-operating, better-feeling body. These food choices are a fast track to not just preventing, but reversing disease, especially coronary artery disease. You can expect to lose weight, build strong bones, get more oxygen to your muscles so you can tackle and complete your day-to-day tasks in record time, sleep much more soundly, and, yes, enjoy time in bed with your partner.

A longer life. Your life will seem longer, but it will also most likely BE longer, because you will be enjoying it more. A host of studies say that switching to fresh, plant-based foods can add at least a decade, and perhaps a good bit more, to your lifespan.

Money in your pocket. I can hear you saying, "Yeah, right." Take a look at your grocery bills for a month, and see how much you're spending on meat. Compare the cost of a pound of meat with a pound of lentils. Some claim you can save $4,000 a year just by turning from four-legged food to the kind with stalks and leaves. Others say probably not, but even they agree you'll save in the neighborhood of $750. Remember you don't need a ranch to grow your own veggies. Just like any do-it-yourself project, this is a way to save while you're having fun and stirring your creative juices.

A better world. In addition to saving yourself and your family from all the heavy metals and toxins found in meat, you'll be taking giant steps toward reducing famine and pollution. Did you know that nearly ¾ of the grain produced in the United States goes to feed animals? That could feed hundreds of millions of people in this country, or, alternatively, boost the trade balance significantly. And, of course, if you're an animal lover, you need only do a little research to find out about crowded conditions and pesticides in food on factory farms. And then there's the fact that those same farms produce enough chemical and animal waste runoff to create one of the greatest threats to clean water in our world today.

It's your body, your life, your world. Now's the time to round the bases by improving all three. Make it your home run!

Foreword

I knew that I had found something special the first time I asked Jude Toscano for a massage. Let's face it, at a couple of inches more than six feet, the kind of strong will people talk about being typical of the Dutch and a real zeal to be sure any massage was a plus before or after a tennis match, I was not the easiest person to wander into her wellness center. Quickly I realized that whatever the task – for me, massage then consultation on how to treat allergies and finally an overall wellness plan – hers is a forthright, and fun-filled approach, as thoughtful as it is thorough. Where the normal practitioner can seem informed, but insistent, she makes you believe (no doubt, because it is true) that once you've started listening to your body and harnessing what it can do, you are on your way to a different kind of life.

No life is without challenge and no challenge is without stress – even the kind that ends up with your holding a trophy. I have yet to meet a committed athlete who does not want to aim for his or her personal best. Most of us have learned that "no pain, no gain" is not enough. In fact, it's not even accurate. You don't need a $1,000-a-day spa or a 350-page book. This slim volume is chock-full of great information presented with Jude's trademark focus on fun.

Sean and I run a tennis camp less than an hour from one of Jude's clinics, a special boon now that we've become friends. I've tasted some of this food – you won't be disappointed.

Brenda Shultz McCarthy,
former top ten Women's Tennis Association tour player in singles and
doubles two-time Olympian

Celebrate Life!

Welcome to your best life! Now is the time to harness what you already know, learn what you have missed before and experience your own personal wellness as a result of deliberate effort, wise choices, and conscious, personal joy. This book is designed to help educate you about the choices you can make to improve your digestion and ultimately your life. You will learn about the inter-relationship between what you think and what you eat, and from that, move through each day with grace and ease.

Your body is brilliant. Your life is creative and organic. When you eat to fit your body's specific needs, you regain and enhance your energy and harness your health. It takes wisdom and willpower. You probably already have more of both than you acknowledge. Otherwise, you wouldn't be reading this!

In this book, I hope to share my own experiences and the wisdom I have gained by studying, working with patients, and focusing on my own personal food and lifestyle choices. What I ask you to do is reach for the best. Celebrate every delicious day.

What Is Your Relationship with Food?

Every relationship begins with a story. Try to recall your very earliest experiences with food. Did some flavor give you a warm, cozy feeling? Were you scolded and told to eat less or eat more? Maybe you were required to clean your plate or told about the starving children in some other country (which one probably depends on how old you are). Was there a time when you, yourself, were afraid you might not have enough food? Did you get sick from overeating?

My story started when I was a little girl growing up in New Jersey. My grandma came to our house in the country to cook outside under our big apple tree, making scrumptious, rich Italian meals. She fried pumpkin flowers coated with a mixture of bread crumbs, fresh parsley and strong Italian cheeses, and the flavors exploded in our mouths. She combined three different meats and fresh tomatoes from the garden to make tomato sauce and cooked it for five hours. The memory of that aroma takes me right back under the apple tree. Grandma shared her love through food, and it worked. For me, this a memory of pure joy and a feeling of richness.

When I went off to college, I got swept away by the campus scene and lost my connection with food and the earth. I returned home with a degree in art, chronic bladder infections, back and knee pain, and not much hope for relief. Then, a book from the library got me started on fasting, and when I began growing a garden, I found myself becoming aware of the power of nature's bounty and the colorful, nutrient-rich gifts it brings. As I increased my nutrients, I felt better and began to reconnect with myself and the earth.

COOKING UP HEALTH, WELLNESS & JOY !

Today, multiple decades later, I still feel joy when I consciously eat healthy vegan and vegetarian foods. Greens, beans, nuts, and seeds allow my body and mind to float through the day. I don't have sugar swings or unmanageable hormone imbalances, and my strength and volition for life are strong. I stay in balance, get less stressed by events that pop up, and avoid getting sucked into other people's dramas.

According to Gabriel Cousins, M.D., author of *Conscious Eating*, "the food we eat affects our body, emotions, mind and spiritual life." Awareness is the key element here. Our bodies are smart; they show us when food is bad and communicate through different detoxification channels when we are overloaded and out of balance. We just need to breathe, listen and be present.

Joy and Happiness

Listen to your heart, and sing your inner song of joy. Pay attention, and you will notice things that you never noticed before.

Let go, let go, let go, and realize happiness comes when your mind is free from a rigid set of ideas.

How Can You Connect with Your Digestive Health?

Each body has its own sense of awareness and level of tolerance that connects to its own personal digestive health. What some would label "sensitive," I call smart. My body knows instinctively how to heal and what to do when I cut my finger. It also knows how to react to bad food. Give your body absorbable nutrients, adequate rest, and make time to connect with your digestive health.

To give those natural processes the best chance to work their magic, we need to focus not only on *what* we eat, but *how* we eat. We need to choose and chew our fresh, healthy foods, be conscious not to overeat, and remember not to snack throughout the day.

CHOOSE

★ Know what you are eating. Fresh is better, every time, but if you can only get what you need packaged, read labels, and choose wisely to save your body from overworking and having to detoxify chemical additives.

★ Consider taking a probiotic and food-based vitamin daily. (See more on the next two pages.)

CHEW

★ Chewing too fast and/or gulping allows large, hard-to-digest particles of food to enter your stomach and intestines, possibly causing gas and bloating.

FACTS AND INSPIRATION

★ Consciously chewing your food thoroughly allows you to absorb more nutrients, and ease digestion. Think about and connect with the food you are eating to help maintain a healthy weight.

★ Chewing a full minute, until your mouthful of food is liquefied and has lost all of its texture, will allow you to connect with what you are eating. You will feel the sensation of being full and know when to stop eating.

CHALLENGE

★ Eating throughout the day (snacking) puts a stress on the digestive system. You should feel hungry before you eat.

★ Conversely, eating a huge amount at any one meal is asking your digestive system to work too hard. Stop when you feel full – or even when you feel close to being full.

★ Exercise regularly, preferably something that makes you happy. Walking and Qigong are my favorites. Get a dog so you'll need to walk twice a day. Take an exercise class. Try something new.

Paying attention to your body will make a noticeable difference. Pummeled by pain, stress, lack of sleep—any one or a combination—your body will cry for rest. If you fail to heed that cry, you may subject yourself to a chronic illness.

Probiotics on Parade

Digestive health is not something we think about until there is a problem, but a healthy gut is important even when there may be few signs of upset or distress. Scientific studies have revealed that an imbalance in intestinal flora may lead not only to constipation, but mental disorders and a decreased immune system. So what's the preventive? A probiotic supplement is a great first step.

The term "probiotic" was first coined in 1951, probably because of the abuse of antibiotics. A probiotic is a dietary supplement containing live bacteria (as lactobacilli) or "gut flora," as they are called, to support the immune system and help the body digest food for better nutrient absorption.

These friendly organisms may also help fight bacteria that cause diarrhea. Housing a 24'- 30' long multilayer, hose-like muscular organ, the digestive system has been called the "second brain," because it includes 75% of the immune system. This immune response has to do with the gut flora, or the "good bacteria" in the digestive tract.

By destroying good bacteria, processed foods wreak havoc on our ability to properly digest food and create an imbalance that may lead to IBS and constipation, and then much more. Bad bacteria can even affect our appearance and our moods, enough to lead to stress, anxiety, and depression-related behavior.

Also, I learned from a pharmacist friend a very helpful tip. If you're taking an antibiotic, lots of people think that cancels the benefits from probiotics. My recent personal experience says that's not the way it works. Probiotics help prevent a common yeast overgrowth called "candida" that is frequently a most uncomfortable result of antibiotics. Not only does it help to take them, I prefer to double my regular dosage. The trick is to make sure to take your probiotics at least two hours before or after the time(s) when you take your antibiotics.

A Vitamin is a Vitamin is not a (Good) Vitamin

You know that something must be up when the vitamins at the supermarket are less than half the price of the vitamins at the health food store. Marketing? Packaging? Branding?

Could be, of course, but more likely it has to do with the quality of the vitamins you're buying. The trick is to know how to avoid synthetics. Yes, they're often used to increase the potency of vitamin products, but some of them are made from derivatives of coal tar. Hmm, that's the carcinogen residing in cigarette smoke.

So how can you tell. Simple, really.

1. You're home free if the label says "100% natural." Just "natural" doesn't get it. That can be as little as 10 percent. Of course, 100% plant-based works, too.

2. You're looking for food sources, not vitamin names. If you see ingredients such as broccoli, spinach, vegetables, or fruit, that's a good sign. Similarly, if the list of ingredients includes Vitamin X instead of the source, that's a great clue that Vitamin X is synthetic.

3. Become a sleuth for any word that ends in "ide" or "ate." That's a screaming clue that salt products are involved, and those, too are synthetics.

Don't give up! The difference is worth it.

Optimum Health is Yours for the Choosing

Why eat a vegetarian or vegan diet? Well, why not?

According to the Mayo Clinic, one of the most respected health facilities in the U. S., a plant-based diet that emphasizes fruits, vegetables, grains, beans, legumes and nuts is rich in fiber, vitamins and other nutrients. In other words, just what you need to stay healthy longer. Why? You will generally eat fewer calories and less fat, weigh less, and have a lower risk of heart disease than non-vegans do. Plus, it will be easier for you to digest, process, and absorb nutrients. Minerals and vitamins are the main ingredients needed to fuel your electrical system and supercharge your energy.

The way to make the greatest difference in your health is to focus on eating much of your food raw and finding the freshest food you can. Vitamins are lost from heat in the cooking process, while minerals and proteins are often amplified and condensed. Nutrients are also lost when food is harvested, shipped, and not eaten for 7 to 10 days, organic or not.

Nothing will benefit human health
and increase chances of survival for life on earth
as much as the evolution to a vegetarian diet.
~ Albert Einstein

A Plan for the Energetic, Enriched Life

Consciously choosing a vegetarian or vegan lifestyle way of eating isn't that hard if you begin with a sound plan and are ready with the answers to questions people are going to ask you about your new-found energy and diet choices.

"How will you get enough protein?"
Did you know all vegetables contain protein? Vegetable proteins are easier to digest; they require less processing so our bodies more easily absorb amino acids, the building blocks of health. I have more energy because my body isn't working so hard to process animal protein.

"What do you eat besides vegetables?"

There are so many choices if I pair my favorite vegetables with spices and a good gluten-free bread and protein from nuts, seeds and beans. I love making smoothies and soups!

"What do you order when you go out to eat?"

I look over the menu, and I take a moment to think about what I would cook with the ingredients listed in the menu selections. Sometimes a special item will have sautéed spinach or asparagus, and I will mix and match to create something new. I also plan ahead and look for healthy restaurants.

"What do you do when you are invited to dinner?"

I make the biggest, best salad that is seasonal and fresh, and I take it as a hostess gift. It is greeted with surprise and gratitude, and puts a vibrant, healthy dish on the table for everyone to enjoy.

Life in Balance: Acids, Alkalines and You

Everybody has an acid/alkaline balance called "pH." The body's pH is influenced by emotional stress, toxic overload, acid-forming foods and acid-forming drinks.

Your body constantly balances the pH ratio between positively charged ions (acid-forming) and negatively charged ions (alkaline-forming).

Building diet choices around alkaline-forming foods will get you eating more vegetables and may even help you lose weight. A good rule to follow in the beginning is a 60 percent alkalinity to 40 percent acidity ratio of foods and drink. Once you understand the concept and know how to pick and organize your food choices, an 80 percent alkalinity to 20 percent acidity is an ideal ratio to maintain.

Paying attention to how your body feels (Is your energy up or down?) with different food combinations and ratios, and "checking in" regularly will get you on the road toward optimal digestion. The purpose of all this is to digest nutrients so you will absorb them.

An easy way to start is to think vegetables first. Look in the refrigerator and make a plan to shop for food more often, at least two times a week. Ask the produce manager at your local grocery store when the truck delivers. Fresh vegetables always taste better. If you are overwhelmed by too many greens, freeze them or make a blended soup.

Be aware of the best combinations of food, too. Here's a basic list to get you going:

Combine proteins with green leafy and non-starchy vegetables.

Put nuts and seeds on a salad.

FACTS AND INSPIRATION

Eat tasty seed cheeses with asparagus and spinach salad.

Enjoy baked or roasted potatoes with a full cup of steamed green beans and a side of raw or steamed zucchini squash.

Dig into a big, green leafy salad with fresh herbs topped with beans or steamed frozen peas.

Give crunch and character to steamed broccoli and cauliflower, by topping them with spicy soaked and toasted nuts and seeds. Include a salad on the side.

Or try cooked and cooled lentils tossed in spicy vinaigrette on top of a big green leafy salad.

Then there are some combinations to avoid. Here are five simple rules:

1. Eat protein with green, leafy vegetables—no starches and with no fruit, except avocados or coconut.
2. Best not to eat any kind of FRUIT with STARCH.
3. Best not to eat ACID and SWEET FRUITS together.
4. Best not to eat FRUITS and VEGETABLES together.
5. Eat melons alone or leave them alone.

Tooling Around

My favorite kitchen tools are quiet and shiny. Seriously, I love little scoops that mold things and cookie cutters that shape things. I use shredders and graters and potato peelers. Oh my!

Also, I use measuring spoons when I create a baked mookie or cookie recipe. If I don't, I can never seem to repeat the recipe. I have a sticky note pad near me to write the ingredients down.

Recipes for soups and salad dressings are guidelines, because the flavors of raw, fresh ingredients change with age and season.

The appliance I use the most in the kitchen is the food processor. Once you know what you are doing with a food processor, you can perform many tasks. If you work dry to wet, using the processor to grind and chop first, you will save time and make clean up easier.

The best blender you can afford is a must for a smooth soup that marries flavor to create an explosion in your mouth. Once you know your tools and realize your favorite flavors, kitchen creativity is limitless and fun.

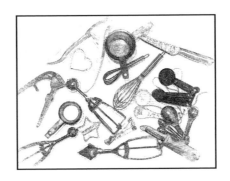

The Power and Pleasure of Preparation

Produce is the food I shop for most frequently, so start getting used to going to buy produce two to three times a week. Buy local organic produce when you can visit where it is grown. It is important to know the person who grows the food you eat.

Pay attention to the color, firmness and freshness of what you are buying. Scan recipes and plan ahead or make sure to eat what you buy. I work at using up what's in the refrigerator by planning salads and making notes. This makes your dinner decisions less stressful. I also appreciate a sense of anticipation. Because of that, I think a moment about creating a certain dish or meal and how to organize it into my busy schedule. Preparing food is fun if you have the time and balance of ingredients to create an explosion of flavors and a balance of nutrients.

A few tricks I have discovered to use up excess produce are:

- ☆ Make a green smoothie.
- ☆ Freeze greens raw in serving-size plastic bags or containers to use in a smoothie at another time.
- ☆ Saute lettuce greens with garlic onion and olive oil.
- ☆ Keep things on hand that you like and are familiar with.
- ☆ Make healthy salad dressings ahead so you can have a salad for a snack.

And remember, if you are reaching for an unhealthy choice, drink water! Chances are you are thirsty.

Flexibility is a Sign of Health!

These new and different pantry picks are not here to stress you out. Your pantry and food choices are within your grasp if that is what you create and desire. With all the research and growing awareness about health and longevity, you come to realize everything changes.

We probably shouldn't live by lab tests and research alone. It is our individualized choices that matter. Our bodies have a muscle or tissue memory, but the memory of Grandma's cooking goes far beyond her culinary skills. That memory comes straight from your heart.

Also, it is not possible for the items on this list to be the only things you need to have and to buy. As gluten-free vegan awareness grows, most of the products on this list are being found in big box stores. Nearly all are available in health food stores. The list keeps growing, *See pages 157-158.*

Superfoods are in abundance. Try shopping, researching and ordering on line!

Let's Talk About Ingredients
(otherwise known as some of my favorite Super Foods)

In a conversation with a friend, Pamela Peeke, M.D., author of a number of best-selling health and fitness books, was asked if supplements—vitamins, minerals, etc.—were really necessary. When she began her response, she pointed out that if we could eat as our grandmothers did, the answer would be a simple "No." Today, though, much of the soil in which our food is grown has been stripped of many nutrients. Certainly, the best answer is to grow your own, if you can. From garden to table is a straight shot for optimum nutritional value, especially when that's not via the stove or microwave! But cooked or raw, the choice of fresh vegetables and carefully selected spices is important. This list includes those most experts consider the superstars. It is organized alphabetically, except for the grouping of three especially powerful foods at the end.

ASPARAGUS, A VEGETABLE WITH BENEFITS!

Nutritionaldata.com labels asparagus as a good source for minerals, fiber, and vegetable protein. Research also indicates that it has the most glutathione, an anti-cancer ingredient and antioxidant, of any other vegetable, or fruit, for that matter.

Low in fat, high in fiber, this green sprout is anti-inflammatory, good for digestion, and helpful in the treatment of depression. Raw or cooked, it has vegetable proteins.

Asparagus is a natural cleanse or flush for the kidneys, because of its diuretic properties. This means it stimulates urine flow thereby helping to prevent kidney stones.

I love watching this sprout come out of the ground, and reach for the sky, with a new, fresh energy. When you are picking a fresh asparagus shoot, it may snap off and be tempting enough to eat in the garden. Tasting its fresh flavors will make you want to have more asparagus plants. Pay attention to any new shoots popping up overnight.

Dips and blended soups are a great way to get raw nutrient and fresh flavors introduced to your taste buds.

BACOPA, THE HERB OF GRACE

Bacopa monnieri is a creeping perennial herb, commonly called "Brahmi." In India where Ayurvedic medicine is practiced, bacopa is used as a remedy to enhance memory and concentration, and to decrease anxiety.

CHIA SEEDS

Chia is a word from the Mayan language, which means "strength." This tiny seed is a powerhouse indeed, loved by athletes for the wallop it packs. Here's just a partial list of benefits:

- ★ Gel, when we add nut milk to make the perfect pudding

- ★ Gluten-free

- ★ Contains bulking fiber that has energy; add to water or a sports drink

- ★ Won't spike blood sugar

- ★ Slow-burning carbohydrate

- ★ High in antioxidants

- ★ Contains 14 percent protein

- ★ Anti-inflammatory and contains good fats

- ★ Can be used as an egg substitute in baked goods; fats are stable when heated.

RAW COCOA (CACAO)

We all know chocolate lifts our spirits; that's why we love it! We can label cocoa beans Nature's antidepressant. The magazine *Scientific American* states, "Research suggests that beneficial bacteria that reside toward the end of our digestive tract ferment both the antioxidants and the fiber in cocoa." This chemical reaction creates a happy colon, which has been proven to create a happy brain.

Dark chocolate has so many health benefits that books have been written about it. Of course, the darker the cocoa, the more beneficial. Cacao's best nutrient feature is the high amount of antioxidants it contains, way more than berries. Look for a cocoa percentage higher than 72 percent and watch out for added sugar and hydroge-nated oils. Heating and cooking this superfood does denature it. That means, when we heat it, then eat it, nutrients have been lost, and antioxidant amounts are lowered. So consider using raw cocoa in smoothies and spicy raw sweet treats.

DIATOMACEOUS EARTH

Remember on the school ground at recess when one boy told another to "eat dirt." Well, believe it or not, that's not always a bad idea. Food grade diatomaceous earth (DE) is a source of available silica, a mineral we all need. It is a component of collagen, a crucial ingredient in the cells that make up our veins, arteries and tissues. Ask anyone who's considered a facelift!

Many people take 1 teaspoon to 1 tablespoon of DE per day in juice, water, applesauce, yogurt or a protein shake. Why?

- ☆ Sore joints feel better
- ☆ Lowers cholesterol (usually 50-75 points lower)
- ☆ Lowers high blood pressure
- ☆ Keeps blood sugar levels more stable

IMPORTANT: DO NOT HEAT OR COOK WITH DIATOMACEOUS EARTH.

- ☆ More energy

- ☆ Healthier skin, less itching, faster healing, psoriasis gone

- ☆ Calms nerves and promotes better sleep

- ☆ Aids in weight loss

- ☆ Supports detoxification and cleansing of digestive tract

- ☆ Keeps skin hydrated

- ☆ Reduces fine lines and wrinkles

DULSE

Dulse is fast becoming one seaweed that those who have real trouble with its sister plants may come to enjoy or even crave. Harvested in the cool waters of the northern Atlantic and Pacific Oceans from early summer to early fall, it is usually dried immediately. The good news is the dried flakes and powder contain as much nutritional value as the fresh red leaves.

Creative chefs are now using it to replace bacon, with success in the taste category and superiority on the health side of things.

GINGER, THE ULTIMATE SPICY ROOT!

Boasting more than 400 healing properties, super food benefits, and flavor that stimulates digestive juices, ginger is as valuable to your health as water to a sprout. It is a virtual apothecary that you can add to most soups and stir fries and know you will spice things up a bit. Chopping ginger and sprinkling it on top of food before serving is a potent addition. Start using this spicy root with confidence and caution!

Ginger is an anti-inflammatory powerhouse at the digestive level. Decreasing inflammation in our gut improves the ability of our body to absorb essential nutrients, thereby improving cellular function on all levels. Ginger tea will help to spark digestive juices and warm you on the inside. Remember this. Making a healthy food choice is important, but digesting and absorbing nutrients make all the difference, because that is the "root" of how our bodies function. Why not try a cup of ginger tea with a teaspoon of coconut oil in it!

GOJI BERRIES

Also called wolf berries, goji berries come from a shrub native to China, where for centuries they have been eaten because of their reputation for extending life expectancy. For sure, they are loaded with goodies: 21 minerals, 19 amino acids, and a multitude of antioxidants. They help strengthen the immune system, and their vibrant color helps stimulate your taste buds. There is a possibility that they react with certain drugs, so checking with a physician before you eat a lot might be a good idea.

KALE, THE QUEEN OF THE GARDEN GREENS

Kale is so nutrient-packed and easy to grow that abundance often follows. It has almost as much calcium ounce for ounce as milk, and it is high in all the health bells and whistles, too (antioxidants, cruciferous, vitamins, and minerals). Cooking kale makes it easier for us to absorb some of its beneficial nutrients.

The best-tasting kale leaves are small and crisp. You can clean and pack them in baggies stored in the freezer, ready for smoothie use.

You can wash kale and slice it thin for wilting and making a salad. I take out the center stem and just use the leaves for salads, but the stems can be composted, saved in a bag in the bottom of the refrigerator to use when making a vegetable stock, or given to your dog as a healthy treat.

Many kinds of kale prevail! Most supermarkets carry a curly leaf kale that is thick and more shelf-stable. I did some research and found several varieties: walking-stick, thousand-headed, red ruffle and dwarf blue-curled kale. The walking-stick variety can get as tall as 6 feet. The stalk is dried and lacquered to be used as a walking stick.

I prefer growing red Russian kale, because the leaves are thin. It grows easily as a cool weather crop, and prevails in warm weather when I let the weeds grow around it and shade it in mid-summer. (Heat can make it bitter.)

Take a moment to explore the many kinds of kale at the 198,000 sites that come up on the Internet. You can surely find one to enjoy!

WHAT ABOUT ROMAINE?

Use romaine lettuce leaves to roll up seed cheeses (*See page 47.*) and make tasty boats full of salsa! You can sauté the romaine core with your favorite vegetables. Of course, my dog just loves the romaine hull plain!

Nutritional profiles show us that, cup to cup, romaine lettuce boasts 84 minerals and is higher in vitamin A and vitamin C than iceberg lettuce. The thing that concerns me is that romaine lettuce has a long shelf life. We don't know when these nutrient values were measured, certainly not when the lettuce is four weeks old. If you do your homework, you will see that nutrients are lost 20 minutes after cutting. This lettuce may have deceived you. Look for the date, eat fresh, and buy local when possible.

SPROUTED GRAINS

When the conditions are right with just enough water and heat, a seed will sprout. Sprouting involves chemical reactions that dissolve an enzyme inhibitor coating on the seed itself, and release the vital life force of the plant. When the life of the seed begins, vitamins and minerals dramatically increase, starches are converted to maltose, and beneficial enzymes are activated.

The enzymatic process of sprouting makes vitamins, minerals, and proteins more easily absorbed during digestion. The end result: the sprouting process creates a more nutritious grain that is easier to digest; naturally increases the protein content; and decreases the calories and carbohydrates found in the original grain. Anybody who has a hard time getting energy from grains or digesting grains needs to try a sprouted cookie!

WATERCRESS: BEAUTY AND BENEFIT IN A LEAFY PACKAGE

Watercress is a springtime delicacy, a spring tonic, and one of the oldest medicinal vegetables. It grows in large patches on top of the water, taking on the appearance of billowing green cloud formations that invite you to consider a long nap. I once saw an amazing watercress patch, that was 20 feet wide and miles long. It never ended. As I strolled along the riverbed, I was in watercress heaven.

This semi-hearty perennial has been cultivated since the 1800s and can be considered the first fast food! In Victorian times, the spicy little green leafy vine was rolled up, wrapped, and eaten like an ice cream cone. I like watercress in salads, sandwiches, soups, pesto, and spicy green smoothies. It is a great source of iron and iodine. It has more calcium than milk, and more iron than spinach!

While all of the foods in this list assuredly qualify as what health practitioners refer to as "super foods," my favorites are watercress, miso and hemp seeds!

MISO

Unpasteurized miso can be added like bouillon or a stock to soups. With a concentrated flavor much like that of ketchup, Worcestershire or soy sauce, miso enriches and emboldens the flavor of the food in which you use it.

What's more, fine quality, unpasteurized miso is a living fermented food containing digestive enzymes, *Lactobacillus*, and other probiotic microorganisms. It strengthens the power of digestion and aids in the assimilation of nutrients. It should be added at the end of the recipe to preserve these enzyme benefits.

I use South River brand miso. It is made in the traditional fashion with love and guidance and is the only brand I have seen that has a chickpea miso. If you are soy sensitive, chickpea miso is a great choice.

South River Miso Company, Inc.
888 Shelburne Falls Road
Conway, Massachusetts 01341
PH: 413.369.4057
info@southrivermiso.com

RAW HEMP SEEDS — HEMP HEARTS

A super-rich food so far as nutrition is concerned, hemp seeds have a nutty flavor and contain 30 percent protein, omega 3 and omega 6 fatty acids, iron and Vitamin E. They are a dense source of plant-based protein that can be whipped into pesto or eaten by the spoonful.

Try hemp seeds on top of soup or hot and cold cereals. Blend hemp into a smoothie, sprinkle hemp seeds on top of your green leafy salad or try some on ice cream. These seeds lose their good qualities when baked, so eat them raw.

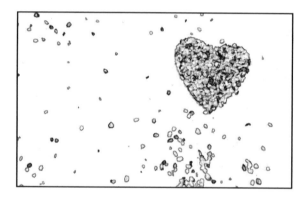

PINK HIMALAYAN CRYSTAL SALT

Pink Himalayan crystal salt is an ancient mineral tonic for health and vitality. Salt in its original form, unlike white table salt, is created in the earth after millions of years of intense pressure. The intense pressure underground forms an organized crystalline structure, which is necessary for information to be absorbed into our cells and utilized. In a potent phrase: pink Himalayan crystal salt is an information carrier.

This special salt also contains about 84 minerals, essential catalysts for the firing of our nervous systems and the involuntary functions of our bodies. Our bodies can be viewed as a large battery and minerals as battery juice. Solé ("so-lay") is a salt water tonic that you can easily make.

Solé Salt Water Tonic

¼ cup pink Himalayan salt
2 cups filtered water

Add the salt to the water and shake to dissolve the salt. Let the mixture rest overnight or until it becomes clear. Add 1 teaspoon to 8 ounces of water and drink once a day.

HIMALAYAN CRYSTAL SALT MINERAL BENEFITS

★ Regulates the water content throughout your body.

★ Promotes a healthy pH balance in your cells, particularly brain cells.

★ Promotes blood sugar health and helps to reduce the signs of aging.

★ Assists in the generation of hydroelectric energy in cells in the body.

★ Aids in absorption of food particles through the intestinal tract.

★ Supports respiratory health.

★ Promotes sinus health.

FACTS AND INSPIRATION

★ Prevents muscle cramps.

★ Promotes bone strength.

★ Regulates sleep by naturally promoting rest.

★ Supports libido.

★ Promotes vascular health.

★ Regulates blood pressure.

Study Proving Health Benefits of Salt

In a 2001 test at the University of Graz, Austria, subjects who drank solé saw significant, positive changes in respiratory, circulatory, organ, connective tissue, and nervous system functions. Patients also reported increases in quality of sleep, energy, and concentration levels, brain activity, weight loss, enhanced consciousness, and noticeable hair and nail growth. For a complete summary of this medical study, please refer to the book *Water and Salt: The Essence of Life*.

COCONUT OIL: THE HEALTHIEST OIL ON EARTH

Yes, it's true: coconut oil boasts and proves to have more beneficial healing properties than any other oil.

Bruce Fife, ND, in his book *Coconut Cures* points out "inflammation of the arteries may explain heart disease in people without other known risk factors. . . ." Healthy oils—and coconut is the healthiest—are our brain food. They promote anti-inflammatory physiological responses that improve our bodies' ability to process nutrients and function more effectively.

In my practice, I often suggest that patients add a tablespoon of coconut oil to a cup of ginger tea to make a super-healthy, anti-inflammatory, and anti-viral drink. Coconut oil also helps calm the digestive tract, so it can help with constipation and inflammatory bowel disorders.

Take a look at all it does, according to recent medical science studies:

- ★ Is completely non-toxic to humans.
- ★ Kills bacteria that cause ulcers, throat infections, urinary tract infections, gum disease and cavities, pneumonia, gonorrhea, and other diseases.
- ★ Kills fungi and yeasts that cause candidiasis, ringworm, athlete's foot, thrush, and infections.
- ★ Expels or kills tapeworms, lice, giardia, and other parasites.
- ★ Boosts energy and endurance, enhancing physical and athletic performance.
- ★ Improves digestion and absorption of nutrients including vitamins, minerals, and amino acids.
- ★ Relieves stress on pancreas and enzyme systems of the body.
- ★ Helps relieve symptoms and reduce health risks associated with diabetes.
- ★ Improves calcium and magnesium absorption.

FACTS AND INSPIRATION

★ Helps protect against osteoporosis.

★ Helps relieve symptoms associated with gallbladder disease.

★ Relieves symptoms of Crohn's disease, ulcerative colitis, and stomach ulcers.

★ Improves digestion and bowel function.

★ Relieves pain and irritation caused by hemorrhoids.

★ Reduces inflammation.

★ Supports tissue healing and repair.

★ Supports and aids immune system function.

★ Helps protect the body from breast, colon, and other cancers.

★ Is heart healthy; improves cholesterol ratio reducing risk of heart disease.

★ Protects arteries from injury that causes atherosclerosis and thus protects against heart disease.

★ Helps prevent periodontal disease and tooth decay.

★ Functions as a protective antioxidant.

★ Helps protect the body from harmful free radicals that promote premature aging.

★ Does not deplete the body's antioxidant reserves like other oils do.

★ Improves utilization of essential fatty acids and protects them from oxidation.

★ Helps relieve symptoms associated with chronic fatigue syndrome.

★ Helps protect against kidney disease and bladder infections.

★ Helps prevent liver disease.

★ Supports thyroid function.

★ Promotes loss of excess weight by increasing metabolic rate.

★ Is utilized by the body to produce energy and is not stored as body fat.

Fats: What to Limit and What to Like

You find a brand of potato chips you've always liked and on the front is emblazoned "Now lower in fat." You're delighted—but then you read the ingredients. You already know that saturated fats, and especially trans fats, are anything but healthy. That means lowering the percentage may well not be enough. The presence of those fats in any amount increases risk of disease. Back on the shelf they go.

So, you should avoid fats entirely? No. Mono-unsaturated and polyunsaturated fats like those in vegetable oils, nuts and seeds actually lower disease risk. It is the trans fats, including partially hydrogenated oils that our bodies don't know what to do with and they wind up causing inflammation and blocking healthy processes. Fats, pasteurized butter, cheese, and ice cream, and most processed foods you also need to avoid.

Dr. Bernard Jenson wrote: "We do not catch diseases. We create them by breaking down the body's natural defenses according to the way we eat, drink, think, and live."

Balance of Ingredients

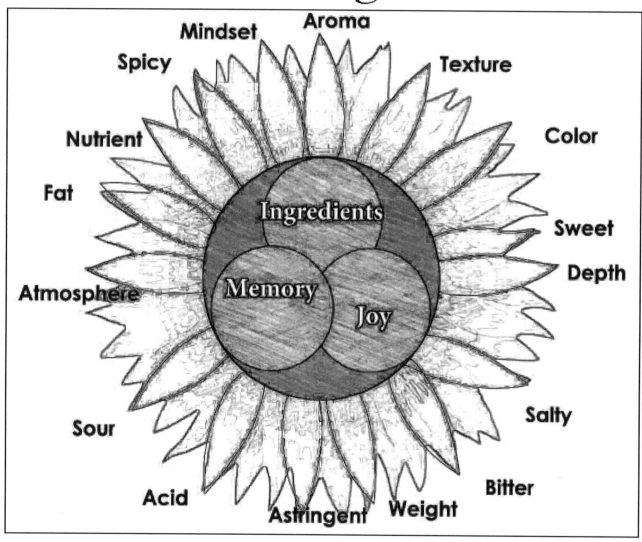

Working on WOW!

We don't really think about it often, we don't talk about it, but what does it take to make a meal you are eating go "WOW" in your mouth and leave you feeling satisfied and full of joy? It is the balance of ingredients, flavors, textures, spices, atmosphere and colors that excite our senses.

Of course, the WOW experience is different for each person, based on his or her individual experience, history, nutritional needs, and sometimes a familiar memory of the way Grandma made it.

Conscious thought and the right ingredients will create something new that takes us to a memory and creates that WOW. See what you can create. I often reach for a soup and a salad dressing that spark my taste buds and fulfill my desire for eating healthy and allow me to experience pure joy!

The recipes in this book are shared with you to help you think out of the box about food (preferably not out of a box) and what you eat. You can easily prepare the soups you will find here in less that 20 minutes, and you may be pleasantly surprised to find that, yes, sweet treats are allowed in a healthy regimen.

Think joy and moderation, trust your gut, and you will find a path that leads you to your desired outcome.

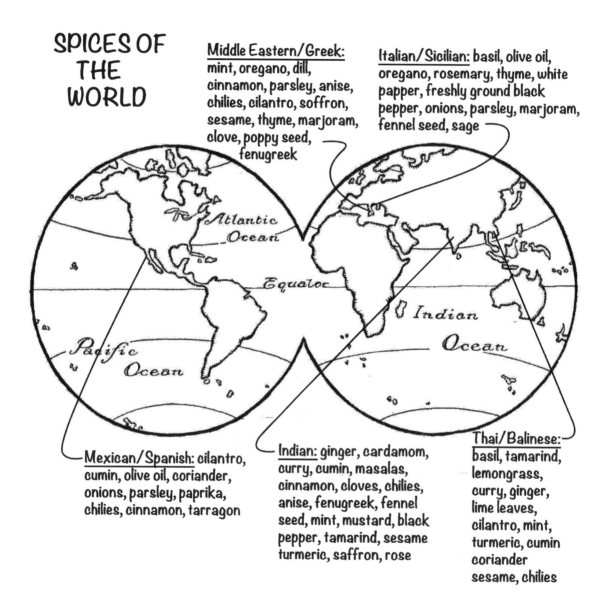

SPICES OF THE WORLD

Middle Eastern/Greek: mint, oregano, dill, cinnamon, parsley, anise, chilies, cilantro, soffron, sesame, thyme, marjoram, clove, poppy seed, fenugreek

Italian/Sicilian: basil, olive oil, oregano, rosemary, thyme, white papper, freshly ground black pepper, onions, parsley, marjoram, fennel seed, sage

Mexican/Spanish: cilantro, cumin, olive oil, coriander, onions, parsley, paprika, chilies, cinnamon, tarragon

Indian: ginger, cardamom, curry, cumin, masalas, cinnamon, cloves, chilies, anise, fenugreek, fennel seed, mint, mustard, black pepper, tamarind, sesame turmeric, saffron, rose

Thai/Balinese: basil, tamarind, lemongrass, curry, ginger, lime leaves, cilantro, mint, turmeric, cumin coriander sesame, chilies

Spices Stimulate the Taste Buds

It's easy to improve your digestion with spices. They stimulate your taste buds and help to increase Hydrochloric acid (HCL), which is necessary for optimal digestion. This is the human body's chief defense system. Stomach acid devours foreign invaders like viruses and bacteria usually found in and on our foods.

Some spices act as carminatives, meaning they help prevent the formation of intestinal gas and stimulate HCL. When HCL levels are low, food remains in the stomach too long, causing acid reflux response. This may not be what every manufacturer and marketer of antacids wants you to know, but it's true. If you have acid reflux, it's from lack of HCL.

Black pepper, sometimes called the "king of spices," is just such a carminative. Cardamom and ginger, common in Indian cooking, can also be used to counteract heartburn, nausea, bloating and gas.

It interests me that different spices are found in cuisines from around the world. Often, it is the memory of a family meal or of a special evening experienced away from home that gets us salivating and thinking, "Oh, I feel like Italian food tonight."

SNACKS

Why Soak Nuts and Seeds?

Raw nuts and seeds are coated with enzyme inhibitors that make them hard to digest and prevent our digestive systems from absorbing nutrients. This coating also prevents the seed from growing. When a seed sprouts, it contains a new life force energy and concentrated nutrients.

Soaking nuts and seeds increases our ability to digest them and allows nutrients to be assimilated. Soak your seeds in water a minimum of six hours, or overnight in the refrigerator. Rinse seeds several times and look for small pebbles. Toss your seeds in your favorite spices and dehydrate or bake them in the oven.

A Few Healthy Snack Ideas

HEALTHY PROTEIN SNACKS

¼ cup almonds
¼ cup hemp seeds
¼ cup sunflower seeds
¼ cup pumpkin seeds
¼ cup tempeh

HEALTHY VEGETABLE SNACKS

green beans, raw or lightly steamed
broccoli florets
zucchini slices
cucumber slices
celery sticks

LOW SUGAR SNACKS

avocado
raspberries
strawberries
blackberries

HAPPY SNACKS!

1 cup nuts or seeds, or mix & match (Pumpkin seeds are my favorite.)
2 Tbs Bragg Liquid Aminos
Sprinkle of cayenne pepper
Sprinkle of pink Himalayan salt

Soak nuts 48 hours; soak seeds 6 hours in filtered water in the refrigerator. Rinse and drain. Toss in Bragg Liquid Aminos. Spread out on a baking tray and sprinkle with cayenne pepper and salt. Bake at 350° for 20-30 minutes, turning the seeds with a spatula and shaking the pan so the seeds separate and brown evenly. These are the perfect road trip food! Serves one or many.

TO KALE OR NOT TO KALE – THAT IS THE PESTO

Pesto spreads have always been a favorite of mine, and although I've created many different ones, I don't think I invented them. I'm sure someone else was out of an ingredient or, as in my case, wanted a nutrient-rich and dairy-free spread that tastes good, has protein, and can be in the refrigerator ready to snack on. Don't get bogged down with specific recipes; have fun! Any nut or seed and any green can be whipped up to create a new spread. Until you try it, you won't know if you like it.

PRESTO! KALE PESTO

1 cup sunflower seeds, soaked in water overnight or a of minimum 6 hours
4 cups fresh kale, washed and dried with stems removed, cut into 1"-2" pieces
3 cloves garlic
2 Tbs olive oil
2 Tbs water
juice of 1/2 lemon
½ tsp pink salt
freshly ground black pepper or a sprinkle of cayenne

Drain and rinse sunflower seeds. Using a food processor, process kale until finely chopped and almost whipped, then place it in a bowl. Process the sunflower seeds the same way, scraping down the sides of the processor to chop evenly. Add to the processed kale and stir together. Process the garlic, olive oil, lemon juice, water and salt, then place 2-3 spoonsful of kale-sunflower mix at a time back into the processor and whip. Serves 4.

I like a thick pesto spread, but you can add more water or oil if you want the consistency of your pesto thin for a sauce or salad dressing.

BROCCOLI PESTO

4 cups broccoli
4 cloves garlic
1 cup fresh basil
¼ cup freshly grated Parmesan cheese or ¼ cup nutritional yeast or vegan cheese substitute
4 Tbs olive oil

Make this recipe with a tight, farm-fresh head of broccoli, cutting off most of the stems and cutting the florets into 4 parts. Chop the garlic and basil into small pieces. Place all ingredients in the food processor and whip to preferred consistency. I chop the ingredients before putting them in the food processor to achieve a fluffy, even consistency. A couple of great ways to eat this: on top of sliced tomatoes; on top of whole wheat pasta or new zucchini pasta; or topped with lemon juice and a bit of freshly made lemon zest, simply done by grating some of the lemon rind on top. Serves 4.

PARSLEY AND SUNFLOWER SEED PESTO SPREAD

4 cups parsley leaves (2 bunches)
1 cup soaked raw sunflower seeds, soaked overnight in water
3 cups filtered water
¼ cup cold-pressed olive oil
2 medium-sized garlic cloves
juice of 1 lemon
¼ tsp salt

Soak the raw sunflower seeds in a glass jar filled with 3 cups filtered water in the refrigerator overnight. Using a strainer, rinse the sunflower seeds before you use them, and let them drain. Remove the leaves from the parsley stems, then rinse and pat dry with paper towel. Place the parsley in a 6-cup food processor; if you have a smaller food processor, you can make smaller batches. Whip the parsley until smooth with an even consistency, scraping the sides of the processor basket. Add the soaked, rinsed, and drained sunflower seeds, olive oil, garlic, juice of 1 lemon, and the salt. Process until green and smooth. Serves 4.

"I am working with the enthusiasm of a man from Marseilles eating bouillabaisse, which shouldn't come as a surprise to you because I am busy painting huge sunflowers."

~ Vincent Van Gogh

ASPARAGUS SPREAD

Maybe you have a patch of asparagus, or maybe you went to the market and the asparagus looked beautiful! This is a great way to try something new or use up those extra lovely green asparagus stalks you picked.

1 bunch of asparagus (about 4 cups
    chopped)
2 cloves of garlic
3 Tbs vegan mayonnaise
¼ tsp dry mustard
1 Tbs honey
Himalayan pink salt to taste

Rinse asparagus, then dry with paper towels. Drying the asparagus is important, because the processor can chop it into nice-size pieces (and not puree).

Cut off about 3" of the bottom. (It is tough and woody.) Cut the stalks into 1" pieces. Place in food processor, chop, add garlic, chop again. Then add dry mustard, honey and mayonnaise and whip to your preferred consistency.

Serve this on thinly sliced sprouted bread, herb crackers or a green leafy salad topped with Spicy Toasted Walnuts! Serves 2.

To keep asparagus longer in the refrigerator, cut the bottoms off and place in a bowl of water with a pinch of Himalayan pink salt.

SEED CHEESE WITH FLAIR TIMES FOUR

1 cup sunflower seeds, soaked a minimum of 6 hours in filtered, unchlorinated water
2 Tbs olive oil
Up to 2 Tbs filtered water to achieve preferred consistency
¼ tsp Himalayan pink salt or to taste

Blend the seeds and olive oil in a food processor. Add water to achieve the desired consistency. Add salt to taste, and then put into a bowl or mold and serve! Serves 4.

This is a vegan seed cheese that can be eaten flavored or plain on a spicy cracker. This recipe can also be watered down to create a dip or used as a creamy alternative in a salad dressing.

Here are some suggestions for flavors that will spice up your life!

Italian Seed Cheese

3 hydrated sun-dried tomatoes
¼ tsp dried oregano
¼ tsp dried basil

Greek Seed Cheese

juice of 1 lemon
¼ tsp dried oregano
¼ tsp dried onion flakes
¼ tsp dried garlic flakes

Indian Curried Seed Cheese

¼ tsp garam masala
¼ tsp curry
3 turns fresh ground pepper

Use cookie cutters to create vegetable chips!   Take your seed cheese on a picnic. It travels really well!

BEET HUMMUS

You can't beat the color and flavor of this! It's a great party pleaser and will definitely show off your talent to spice things up a bit!

2 cups raw beets (peeled & chopped)
2 garlic cloves
1 15-oz. can chickpeas (drained and rinsed)
1 Tbs tahini
1 Tbs olive oil
2 Tbs lemon juice
1 Tbs tamari
2 Tbs filtered water
½-1 tsp Himalayan salt to taste

Using your lovely food processor, process the beets first. Add ingredients one at a time until you have created a SMOOTH, hot pink masterpiece that tastes both earthy and exquisite. Serves 4.

* If you don't have all these ingredients, you can use store-bought hummus, add the raw beets, some good salt, and maybe another garlic clove. See what you can create!

* This recipe can be diluted with more water and made into a healthy, colorful salad dressing or used as a protein-packed topper.

DIVINE SWEET POTATO HUMMUS

This creamy savory surprise is a treat to bring to any party. It adds color and nutrient values with little effort!

3 cups raw sweet potato or yams, peeled and chopped
4 cloves garlic
1 pkg store-bought traditional hummus (10 oz.)
1 Tbs olive oil
2 Tbs lemon juice
1 Tbs nama shoyu (or good quality soy sauce)
¼ cup filtered water
1½ tsp sea salt
1½ tsp ground cumin
½ tsp cayenne pepper
¼ tsp ground coriander

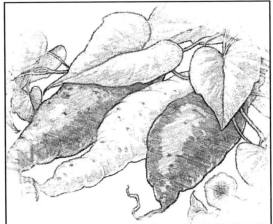

Mix fresh spices and salt together in a small bowl. Place yams into a blender or food processor in small amounts. Add additional ingredients one at a time, leaving the mixed spices until last. Blend until smooth. This will evenly distribute ingredients and cream the hummus. Add more water if you would like your hummus for a dip. Garnish with fresh parsley. Serve with fancy-cut zucchini, your favorite crackers, or chips. Serves 6.

Additional Serving Suggestions:

* Vegetable wraps with sweet potato hummus
* Big green leafy salad with sweet potato hummus dip as salad dressing topped with a few dried cranberries!

KNOCK YOUR SOCKS OFF SALSA

3 cloves of garlic
1 cucumber
2 cups flat-leaf parsley
1 white onion
1 red onion
3 cups firm tomatoes
2 Tbs apple cider vinegar
juice of 2 limes

<u>Himalayan salt to taste when serving.</u> (The vinegar will make these ingredients weep, and you will get a soupy salsa if you use to much salt.)

Chop garlic, parsley and onion individually in food processor. Chop by hand cucumber and tomatoes. Combine all chopped ingredients in large bowl and add lime juice and vinegar. Happily stir together and serve with veggies or chips of choice.

SOUPS

Cooked soup or raw soup? That is the question. Have some fun creating the soups in this section. I chose to share with you some hearty winter favorites and then transitioned them into lovely raw soups.

What is the difference?

Cooked soups use cooked oil and vegetables, usually taking about 45 minutes or more to create. They start with a stock, get richer with age, and are great to freeze and then eat.

Raw soups are really a way to get you to eat more live nutrients and free up your time in the kitchen. Easy to make in a blender, taking about 15 minutes to create and requiring even less time to clean up. Raw soups should be eaten the day you make them. They are really salads turned into warm, spicy smoothies!

Whichever soups you choose, remember to use healthy toppers. They enhance your visual stimulation and spark your taste buds.

Good Idea!

Try making soup or pesto with your backyard weeds! Two greens free and easily found in your backyard include common Purslane and Chickweed.

Purslane

Chickweed

VEGETARIAN MINESTRONE SOUP

2 Tbs olive oil, plus whatever is needed to keep things browning
1 package Tofurkey Vegan Italian sausage, sliced in 1/4" rounds, then cut in half. (This is a soy-based product found in most supermarkets.)
1 small white onion
2 Tbs (about 5 cloves) fresh garlic chopped
2 large celery stalks, cubed
2 carrots, peeled & cubed
1 16-oz. jar tomato basil organic pasta sauce
1 quart water (Rinse out the tomato sauce jar.)
1 16-oz. can garbanzo beans, rinsed
2 6" - 7" zucchinis, quartered and sliced about ¼ inch thick
1 bay leaf
1 Tbs fennel seeds
1 Tbs dried basil
1 tsp Himalayan salt
fresh ground black pepper to taste

Put olive oil in a frying pan and brown the Tofurkey rounds, then remove them and place them in a bigger soup pot. Add onion to frying pan, and when onion color turns translucent, add garlic and brown. Add cooked onion and garlic to soup pot, along with a bit more olive oil, if needed.

Brown celery and carrots in frying pan, and then add to soup pot. Add tomato sauce, bay leaf, water, and beans to the soup pot. Cover and simmer the soup 20 minutes.

Brown the zucchini, and add to the soup pot with fennel seeds, dried basil, and salt. Simmer until zucchini is done, about 20 minutes longer. Taste the soup, adding black pepper and salt, if needed. Serve with crusty cheese bread and a glass of red wine.

COOKING UP HEALTH, WELLNESS & JOY !

Minestrone soup, simply put, is pure joy! Of course, I feel this way about most savory long-cooked stewed vegetarian foods. These are flavors that marry and become rich and hearty, and stick to your ribs.

The word "minestrone," when broken down means "big soup." Historically, this was a soup made with a salt water spelt flour stock and seasonal vegetables. Basically, whatever vegetables were available in the house went into the soup.

I can remember smelling the Italian spices in this soup as a young connoisseur of my grandmother's cooking and later in my sister, Nancie's, kitchen. Nancie taught Italian cooking classes to youngsters for years with the help of my niece, Victoria. Together they successfully mastered the art of Grandma's cooking. I took the memories of these happy spice smells and transformed them into vegetarian delights, which set the stage for vegan raw epiphanies.

VEGAN RAW MINESTRONE SOUP

1 carrot, quartered and sliced thin
1 zucchini, quartered and sliced thin
1 orange, juiced
¼ tsp salt

Place carrot and zucchini in orange juice. Add salt. Wilt 20 minutes. *See "How to Wilt" page 113.*

1 Tbs olive oil
2 Tbs red pepper garlic miso (South River brand) *See Miso information on page 27.*
½ cup sun-dried tomatoes
        (To hydrate, place tomatoes in a jar and cover with warm water.)
2 garlic cloves
1 celery stalk
½ small red onion
½ tsp Himalayan salt
2-3 cups warm water

Place all ingredients in blender or Vitamix and blend till smooth. Add colorful wilted carrots and zucchini. Texture in minestrone soup is important. Top with ground herb garnishes and serve with joy! Garnish with1 tsp. dried basil and 1 tsp. fennel (cracked using a mortar & pestle).   Serves 4.

SINGING PUMPKIN TOMATO SOUP

Don't cook all that pumpkin! Eat some raw; it is awesome!

½ medium onion, chopped
2 Tbs coconut oil
6 sun-dried tomatoes
1 ½ cups vegetable broth
1 ½ cups pumpkin
2 Tbs real maple syrup
salt to taste (Start with 1/8 tsp)

Wash and cut the pumpkin. You don't have to peel it. You can steam it on your stovetop or bake it in the oven, covered, at 350° until soft. Then peel it and measure. (You may also use plain canned pumpkin.) Dice onion and sauté in oil until clear.

Blend cooked pumpkin with vegetable stock, adding sun-dried tomatoes, a bit of salt, and maple syrup. Check for creamy consistency. Blend a few more minutes, if needed, and serve topped with Happy Snacks (soaked and roasted pumpkin seeds) sprinkled on top. Serves 4.

CREAMY RAW PUMPKIN TOMATO SOUP

Sweet and savory is the goal; an explosive autumn glow followed by a warm calm—YUM!

4 cups chopped raw tomato
5 halves sun-dried tomatoes, hydrated in warm water
4 cups raw peeled pumpkin, cubed into about 1" squares
3 cups hot water
2 Tbs olive oil
½ tsp garam masala
1 pinch of hing (Also called "asafetida," which is known in certain communities for its old dirty sock smell.)
1 pinch ground cayenne pepper
1 Tbs xylitol or stevia to taste
salt to taste

Chop fresh tomatoes. Peel pumpkin and cut into about 1" cubes. Cut up sun-dried soaked tomatoes. Place all in a high-powered blender or Vitamix. Top with hot water, add oil, and spices. Blend until creamy and taste. Adjust the spices and salt until you enjoy the flavors and achieve a taste that pleases you.   Serves 4.

What time is dinner?

HOT TOMATO CURRY SOUP

3 fresh ripe tomatoes
5 sun-dried tomatoes, hydrated,
        by pouring hot water over the dried tomatoes
3 cloves fresh garlic
1 ripe avocado
¼ tsp curry
¼ tsp black pepper
¼ tsp Himalayan pink salt
2 cups hot coconut milk
dash of cayenne (to taste)

Warm the unsweetened coconut milk on the stove top. Cut and remove the cores or stems of tomatoes. Add tomatoes and all the remaining ingredients to the blender. When coconut milk is warm and just about to scald, add it also to the blender and whip to a smooth creamy consistency. Taste and see if you have added enough salt and spice. Garnish with fresh chopped parsley and sliced cherry or grape tomatoes.
Serves 4.

Cooking is like love.
It should be entered into
with abandon, or not at all.

~ Julia Child

GREEN, RED PEPPER MISO SLURP

1 small sweet zucchini
3 cloves garlic
1 red pepper
2 cups spinach
3 green onion bottoms
2 Tbs red pepper garlic miso (South River brand is my favorite.)
¼ tsp pink Himalayan salt
¼ tsp curry
2 cups hot water

It is best to start with all ingredients at room temperature. If you like, you can run hot water over all ingredients to warm them. Warm the miso in the water on the stove. Warm your bowls, too. This keeps a soup made in the blender warm and more flavorful. Wash and semi peel zucchini; cut into 1" pieces. Peel 3 cloves garlic. Wash and remove the stem from a sweet red pepper. Cut up and place with all the other ingredients in blender. Blend until you achieve a smooth, slurpy consistency. Oh my! Serves 4.

DANCING SOUP

4 Tbs olive oil
1 cup onion, chopped fine
4 garlic, chopped fine
1 cup celery, chopped, diced, or processed
3 cups sweet potatoes,
      peeled and cut into bite-size cubes
1 cup sun-dried tomatoes
2 15-oz. cans of chickpeas (low sodium, organic)
2 cups fresh kale
8 cups vegetable stock
dash of cinnamon
dash of cayenne
2 bay leaves
1 tsp basil
1 tsp pink salt
1 tsp turmeric
2 tsp paprika
1 Tbs tamari

Cut the onion into 1" blocks, process in food processor and place in olive oil to start sautéing. Process the garlic and add it to the onion along with the bay leaves. Stir a bit, coating everything with oil, and simmer until the onion turns clear. Add celery and sweet potato cubes, cooking about 15 minutes on low heat. Stir occasionally, but not too much, or you will mash the sweet potatoes. Add sun-dried tomatoes, chickpeas, kale and vegetable stock. Simmer 15 minutes. Add cinnamon, cayenne, basil, salt, turmeric, paprika and tamari. Simmer 10 more minutes. Taste the explosion of flavors and see the rich colors that made me dance when I first created this soup!   Adding spices last gives the soup its secret dancing powers. Serves 6.

SOUPS

As you may have noticed, I like to spice things up a bit!

I do that because the more I use spices and herbs, the more fun I have experimenting with them.

Dancing soup is a result of having fun, creating joy, and an epiphany with spices. If you slow down and taste this soup, the sweet potatoes give it a bit of sweetness, followed by the sun-dried tomato flavor that stands alone for a second and then marries with other flavors as you chew. Chickpeas are a nutty addition, then spices prevail, and then kale greens.

What a way to stimulate your sense of taste and make you want to do a happy dance!

HAPPY & RAW DANCING SOUP

With this soup, blend the first part of the ingredients and then add the kale leaves and chopped sweet potatoes. Blend just enough to marry the flavors without losing the texture.

2 Tbs coconut oil
1/4 cup red onion
2 garlic cloves
1/4 cup sun-dried tomatoes cut or julienne pre-cut
     (hydrated in a jar from the store)
2 Tbs South River chickpea miso
2 cups hot water
dash of cinnamon
dash of cayenne
½ tsp dried basil
½ tsp salt
½ tsp turmeric
1 tsp paprika
1 Tbs tamari
2 cups fresh kale
1 cup sweet potatoes, peeled and cut into bite-size pieces
1 fresh tomato, chopped to add texture and a fresh flavor

As with most blended soups, start with the ingredients at room temperature. Measure the top ingredients into the blender or Vitamix. Blend until smooth, creating a solid base. Add kale and sweet potatoes, and process to distribute them and create a texture. Then pour into a bowl and top with fresh-cut tomato. Also consider toppers of hemp seeds and a few dehydrated onion rings. Still dancing? Serves 2—takes two to tango!

SPICY WATERCRESS SOUP

1 Tbs coconut oil
¼ cup red onion
2 cups watercress, cleaned and de-stemmed
¼ tsp pink Himalayan salt
½ cup soaked pecans (soaked in filtered water overnight)
dash of cayenne pepper
2 cloves garlic
1 tsp mustard seeds

Save some sprigs of watercress to use as garnish before serving.

Place ingredients in blender or Vitamix. Blend to a smooth consistency and taste to see if you think it needs more salt or cayenne. Be careful with the cayenne—you can always add more when you are at the table. Don't forget the garnish! Serves 4.

ENLIGHTENED COCONUT SOUP

2 Tbs coconut oil
1 Tbs grated ginger
1 Tbs maple syrup
1 tsp curry
3 cups (unsweetened) coconut milk warmed
1 Tbs fresh lime juice
¼ tsp Himalayan pink salt
2 Tbs chia flour (ground chia)

Garnish:
2 Tbs chopped fresh cilantro leaves
lime zest

Place coconut milk in a pot on the stove. Turn heat on low. Add other ingredients to a high-powered blender. When coconut milk is warm and just about to scald, remove from heat, and carefully pour it in the blender on top of all the other ingredients. Whip your soup to perfection. Taste it to see if you think it needs anything. Blend again, about 2 minutes. Taste it once more before you serve it to make sure there is enough salt. Top with chopped cilantro and a bit of lime zest. Serves 4.

WOW! This soup may take your tastebuds to a new level of awareness. Enjoy!

PSEUDO POTATO LEEK SOUP

Leek Stock: 3 leeks, tops washed and chopped into 2" pieces. Bring to a boil, then reduce to a simmer in stock pot with 6 cups water. Simmer 3 hours. (I use a crockpot and let this simmer all day.) Strain.

1 cup unsweetened organic coconut milk, room temperature
3 cups warm leek stock
¼ cup chia flour
¼ tsp garlic powder
½ tsp pink Himalayan salt
2 Tbs dandelion leek miso (South River Brand)
1 grind of fresh ground black pepper
3 small green onions, chopped neatly for garnishing

Place all ingredients in blender or Vitamix. Pour warm leek stock over top. Blend to achieve creamy consistency. Before serving, top with just enough green onion or spiralized zucchini to add color and a bit of raw energy. Serves 4.

POTATO, TOMATO LEEK SOUP

First, make the stock. Chop 3 leeks into 2" pieces. Bring to a boil in stock pot with 6 cups water, then reduce to simmer for 3 hours. (I simmer all day in a crockpot.) Strain or not? Strain the leeks out and use the liquid stock to make this memorable soup.

1 cup unsweetened organic coconut milk,
    room temperature or warmed with leek stock
3 cups leek stock
2 white potatoes
2 Tbs chia flour
¼ tsp garlic powder
½ tsp dehydrated onion flakes
½ tsp pink Himalayan salt
2 Tbs tomato red pepper miso
3 hydrated sun-dried tomatoes

Create the leek stock. Good job! Peel and cube potatoes into bite-size pieces. Boil in leek stock for 20 minutes until soft. Add the coconut milk and heat for about 5 minutes until everything is warm.

Creaming some of the soup gives it an added texture, and at the same time prevents it from being all pureed. Place ¾ of the warm stock with potato cubes cooked, in a high-powered blender with the rest of the ingredients on the recipe list. Blend to achieve creamy, smooth consistency. Then mix creamed ingredients with cooked potatoes.

Garnish with thinly sliced leek bottom, cut in rings, and a dash of paprika for color. Serves 4.

FANTASTIC! LIP-SMACKING GREEK LEMON SOUP

Wilted carrot and celery topper!

      1 stalk of celery, 1 peeled carrot, thinly sliced on an angle

Place carrot slices and celery in a bowl. Squeeze the juice of ½ lemon over the veggies, then sprinkle 1 tsp pink salt onto them. Mix and let rest for 20 minutes while you set the table and prepare the soup.

3 cups hot water
½ cup red onion
3 cloves fresh garlic
2 Tbs chickpea miso (South River Brand)
¼ tsp salt
3 Tbs hemp seeds or chia flour (for consistency)
4 sprigs parsley leaves
1 tsp dried lemon thyme
pinch of cayenne
oregano and lemon zest

Mix all ingredients except the oregano and lemon zest in Vitamix or the blender for about 5 minutes. See if more salt or herbs are needed for your taste buds. Pour in lovely bowls and top with wilted carrots and celery. Add a sprinkle of dried oregano crushed between your fingers to activate your heavenly sense of smell. Top with a sprinkle of fresh lemon zest before serving. Serves 4.

LEMON ZUCCHINI SOUP

The cookie cut-out shapes floating on top will make this soup attractive to the eyes as the explosion of flavor grabs your taste buds!

2 zucchini, about 6" long
2 cloves of garlic
¼ cup red onion
½ avocado
½ lemon (juice of)
¼ tsp dried oregano
½ tsp Himalayan pink salt
2 cups hot water

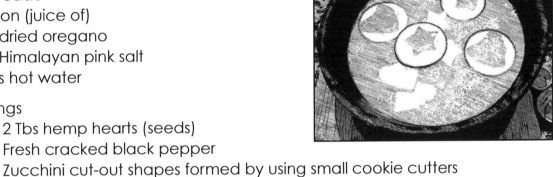

Toppings
    2 Tbs hemp hearts (seeds)
    Fresh cracked black pepper
    Zucchini cut-out shapes formed by using small cookie cutters

Cut up zucchini into 1" pieces; use all extras from the cut-out shapes you created. Place all ingredients in a high-powered blender or Vitamix. Blend ingredients until smooth. Taste to see if you need a bit more salt. Serve in a large flat soup bowl so garnishing shapes have room to float. Serves 4.

To float the zucchini cut-outs on top of your soup, make sure you slice the rounds thinly. These would be great as a pretty topper to spruce up most any favorite dinner!

LUSCIOUS CREAMED SPINACH SOUP

Starting with all ingredients at room temperature and warming the bowls and having the table set will allow you to serve a healthy warm soup. This will also build your anticipation and give you a presentation that is full of color and warmth.

2 cups unsweetened coconut milk (warmed but not scalded)
1 Tbs olive oil
2 Tbs chia flour
1/3 cup macadamia nuts
3 cloves garlic
3 cups organic baby leaf spinach
½ tsp salt
1 tsp dried lemon thyme

Place coconut milk in a pot on the stove and turn the heat on low.

Add all other ingredients to a high-powered blender. When coconut milk is warm and just about to scald, place it in the blender on top of the other ingredients. Whip your soup to perfection, about 5 minutes.

Serve with a large, crunchy salad. Garnish with fancy large organic coconut flakes. Eat slow and savor the flavors. Serves 4.

Anyone who tells a lie
has not a pure heart,
and cannot make
good soup.
~
Ludwig van Beethoven

GOLDEN GARLIC SOUP
(It's hearty and healthy.)

2 Tbs coconut oil
10 garlic cloves
1 small onion (about ½ cup)
2 bay leaves
4 cups vegetable broth
3 medium white potatoes, peeled and cubed
1 15-oz. can of cannelloni beans, rinsed and drained
½ tsp dried oregano
1 tsp dried basil
2 tsp parsley

In a large stock pot, sauté chopped onion and garlic in coconut oil. Simmer until the onions are clear and the aroma makes you smile! Stir in the bay leaves and sauté until they are coated with oil and change color. Pour in vegetable broth and bring to a boil. Add potatoes, and bring back to a boil. Simmer 15 minutes. Add rinsed cannelloni beans and stir. Take out 1 cup of the broth/bean mixture, and place in the blender. Blend to create a creamy base, then pour thickened creamy mixture back in pot. Add fresh herbs if you have them; if not, add dry herbs. Rub and crush herbs in palms of your hands to activate their flavors. Salt to taste. Continue to simmer about 10 minutes. Serves 4.

This soup is great served with a large, fresh, green leafy salad, or a wilted kale salad. It is a hearty soup that's perfect to bring to work the following day.

GINGER ALMOND SOUP

(a blended soup that you will crave)

2 cups unsweetened almond milk
½ cup celery
2 Tbs chia flour
¼ cup unsweetened almond butter
½"-1" piece of fresh ginger root (Reserve half to adjust the amount of ginger root flavor to your preference.)
¼ tsp Himalayan pink salt
1 Tbs maple syrup
1 dash of cayenne pepper (more if you like)
½ cup sliced almonds, browned to garnish soup with color and crunch

Organize all your ingredients then set the table. Place almond milk in a pot on the stove; turn heat on very low. Place ingredients, with exception of toasted almond toppers, into a high-powered blender. When almond milk is warm and just about to scald, remove from heat and carefully pour it in the blender on top of all the other ingredients.

Whip your soup to perfection, tasting it to see if you need more ginger kick. Blend again, about 2 minutes. Taste the soup again before you serve it to make sure there is enough salt. Top with toasted almonds for texture, crunch, and dense, toasted flavors. Serves 4.

CELERY SCHOLAR SOUP

3 ½ cups celery, chopped in 1" pieces
½ cup celery, diced (small cubes) for soup topping
4 cloves garlic
3 cups warm water
3 Tbs chickpea miso (South River brand)
1 tsp Herbamare (a Vogel salt/herb/vegetable mix)
2 Tbs coconut oil (or ¼ cup macadamia nuts creamed to a butter consistency)
salt to taste
2 Tbs bacopa (*See Facts and Inspiration, page 21.*)

Place all ingredients (except the diced celery for topping) in a high-powered blender or Vitamix. Blend to a creamy consistency, about 5 minutes. Top with diced celery and/ or with soaked and roasted spicy pumpkin or sunflower seeds. See Toppers page 106.

RAW KALE SOUP

6 stalks asparagus (thick)
1 red pepper
1 avocado
1 apple, peel if it is not organic
4 cups kale
2 Tbs chickpea miso (South River brand)
2 cups hot water
¼ tsp Himalayan pink salt

It is best to start with ingredients at room temperature. Wash, cut up, core, and chop all ingredients into bite-size pieces. Place in a blender or Vitamix. Whip to a chunky texture. Enjoy!

Soup became a culinary favorite more than 9,000 years ago, during the Neolithic Age, when the practice of boiling meat in water with plants or grains began.

And, of course, it is also part of the Judeo-Christian tradition. In the Genesis story, Esau traded his inheritance for red lentil soup.

GARAM MASALA SUMMER SQUASH SOUP

[spicy (Hot) mixture]

We have two things going on here: making a topper with almond slices and making a soup with soaked almond slices because the almonds really are the protein or meat substitute.

½ cup sliced almonds soaked in filtered water overnight
1 green zucchini squash about 6" long
1 Tbs olive oil
2 cups warm water
½ tsp Himalayan pink salt
¼ cup red onion (Be careful not to put in too much onion.)
2 cloves garlic

Cut the zucchini in bite-size pieces and place in blender or Vitamix with soaked almonds. Add garlic cloves, salt, onion, oil, and water. Blend until smooth consistency. Add salt; blend again. Serve with spicy nut mixture sprinkled on top. If you desire more spice, add a dash of cayenne with the nuts!

Topper

1/8 tsp cardamom seeds
7 black peppercorns
¼ tsp garam masala
¼ tsp ground nutmeg

¼ tsp ground cumin
¼ tsp ground coriander
½ cup sliced almonds

Prepare the first two spices by grinding them in a mortar and pestle; add the ground spices, to the next four and stir with the almond slices. In a frying pan, on moderate heat, brown the spices and almond slices together. This mixture will create the topping that makes this soup sing in your mouth.

GREEN BEAN ALMONDINE

¼ cup toasted sliced almonds
3 cups unsweetened almond milk
2 cups fresh, raw green beans
  (Save a few raw beans to use as garnish for the top of your completed soup.)
¼ cup onion (red, white or green)
1 ripe avocado
1 clove garlic (fresh and big)
dash cayenne
¼ tsp Himalayan salt
pinch coarse black pepper
1 Tbs toasted almonds for topper

Rinse the beans, remove stems, and cut into 1" pieces. Clean the onion and chop. Scoop out the avocado. Peel garlic clove. Place onion, avocado, salt and pepper in Vitamix or blender. Measure almond milk in a small saucepan and place on low heat on the stove top. Continuously keep your eye on this, frequently stirring. Pour warm almond milk over the top of the remaining ingredients and blend until a creamy consistency. Taste the soup to see if it needs more spice for your liking. Pour spectacular soup into bowls and garnish with a string bean cut in half lengthwise, so it floats. Top with a sprinkle of toasted almonds. Serves 3-4.

GREEN BEAN COCONUT WONDER SOUP

3 cups unsweetened coconut milk
2 cups fresh, raw green beans
   (Save a few beans to garnish your completed soup.)
¼ cup onion (red, white, or green)
1 ripe avocado
1 clove garlic (fresh and big)
dash cayenne
¼ tsp Himalayan salt
pinch coarse black pepper
sprinkle of large flake coconut for topping

Rinse the beans, remove stems, cut into 1" pieces. Clean the onion and cut up as well. Scoop out the avocado, peel the garlic clove, add salt and pepper. Place in Vitamix or blender. Measure coconut milk in a small saucepan and place on low heat on the stove top. Continuously keep your eye on this, frequently stirring. Pour warm coconut milk over the top of remaining ingredients and blend to a creamy consistency. Taste the soup to see if it needs more spice for your liking. Pour wonder soup into bowls and garnish with a string bean cut in half lengthwise, so it floats. Top with a sprinkle of fancy coconut flakes. Serves 3-4.

RAW ASPARAGUS SOUP

12 thin stalks asparagus
½ red pepper
2 green onion tops
1 avocado, ripe & sweet
1 apple
4 cups spinach leaves
2 Tbs chickpea miso
4 cups hot water
juice of 1 lemon
¼ tsp Himalayan pink salt

Look for fresh asparagus. When you bring it home, slice 3" off the bottom and place standing up in a bowl of water with a pinch of Himalayan pink salt. The asparagus will hydrate and have more flavor. This is also a good way to keep the asparagus a few days longer in the refrigerator.

It is best to start with ingredients at room temperature. Wash, cut up, core, and squeeze lemon for juice ahead of time. All ingredients should be cut into bite-size pieces. Place in a blender or Vitamix and puree to perfection! Serve with a few asparagus spears on the side. Serves 4.

SCREAMING BLACK BEAN SOUP

1 15-oz. can black beans
2 cups chopped tomato
¼ cup chopped onion
½ cup filtered water
3 cloves garlic
2 Tbs olive oil
2 Tbs chopped fresh parsley
½ tsp Himalayan pink salt
pinch cayenne pepper

Place ½ of the can of black beans and all other ingredients in a blender or Vitamix and blend till smooth. Turn in other half of can black beans into the batch of soup. This will add texture and a bean bite, not found in a pureed soup. Top with fake bacon or spicy dehydrated almonds; recipes found on page 107.

SALADS

Salads are a great base or starter for meals. Toppers can add color and nutrients.

Search for a variety of greens. Look for freshness and buy perky, happy, green leafy vegetables. Do not buy them if they are yellow or wilted. Salad greens lose their nutrients once they are cut from the plant, so the fresher the better.

Textures like the softness of butter lettuce and the crispness of romaine lettuce make a salad. You can top salads with crunchy, toasted, sliced almonds and spicy, happy snacks, and serve with quinoa or rice pasta. Spiralize or wilt vegetables and make homemade salad dressings to drizzle on top of your bed of fresh greens. Why not add cut-up vegetables? They are delicious and nutritious. See what you can create today.

How Do You Make a Healthy Salad?

Salads can be like art, with the beauty coming forth with nutrient-rich color. Eye-catching colors in a salad will draw you in and activate your senses. In chef school, students learn the importance of plate presentation, color, height, portion size, and the shape and size of the plate itself. You can, too!

My happiest, tastiest salads start with my selection of greens. I told someone once that I don't need a big seasonal garden. Instead I need a greenhouse to grow greens and herbs year round.

I love the textures that fresh greens can bring to a salad; I get happy just thinking about it. Don't get me wrong: nothing is as flavorful as a cucumber, fresh picked from the vine that you have been nurturing and watching grow for weeks. But it is the spice and flavor of the variety of greens and herbs in a salad that wake up your senses and open your taste buds.

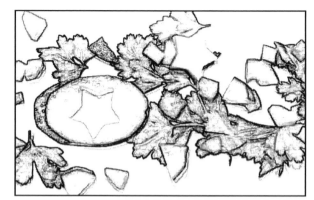

The nutrients found in greens are the power source that feeds our bodies' electrical system. Since vitamins and minerals feed and support our bodies in both antagonistic and synergistic ways, we need to eat them in the most easily absorbed form possible, and greens are packed with the easily absorbed, good stuff.

Start by adding different greens to your salads. Grocery stores and seed companies have a wide selection, if you seek them out. If you live in the country, learn some wild crafting. Chances are you have access to some free greens and can spice up that salad for free.

Purslane is a weed and one of those treats that I find in the garden in the spring and early summer. It has a high concentration of healthy fats and makes a great addition to a salad.

Mache and watercress are two highly nutritious supermarket finds that are also excellent choices.

COOKING UP HEALTH, WELLNESS & JOY !

If you get overwhelmed with greens and can't eat them up fast enough, you can sauté them in coconut oil and spices, or wash and dry them, then freeze them in small plastic bags to throw into a smoothie or soup at a later time. Also, remember you can use any green in a pesto spread, and freeze that for another time as well.

Experiment with green texture and flavor and add your favorite fresh colorful vegetables on top. You can also top with a few soaked and toasted nuts and seeds, or a small amount of homemade salad dressing, and enjoy! There is no right or wrong; just a new pallet of texture, flavor, and color for you to harvest and create. Get creative! You deserve something special, refreshing, and nutrient-rich.

VEGAN CAESAR SALAD

1 head of crisp fresh romaine lettuce, chopped to bite-size (not too big, not too small) pieces.

Dressing (prep together the night before):
½ cup macadamia nuts (ground and soaked overnight in filtered water, a minimum of 4 hours)
1 tsp sprouted mustard seeds (soaked in filtered water overnight, a minimum of 4 hours)
1 cup water
juice of 2 organic lemons
1 Tbs olive oil
1 tsp salt
1 clove garlic
3 pitted dates

Garnish with:
>   thinly sliced red onions
>   dried oregano
>   fresh ground black pepper

In a high-powered blender or food processor, puree soaked nuts, mustard seeds, water, and salt until well mixed. Add the remaining ingredients and blend again until smooth. Using your hands, mix and gently massage the romaine greens with the puree. Sprinkle garnishes on top. Lift with a fork to ever so slightly toss ingredients together. Serves 4.

CARROT SALAD

1 lb. organic carrots, peeled or scrubbed well
2" piece of fresh ginger
¼ cup Bragg Apple Cider Vinegar
¼ cup Bragg Liquid Aminos
1 Tbs Veganaise (Vegan mayonnaise; see recipe under Dressings)
¼ cup organic raisins or currants
¼ cup walnuts

Shred the carrots and ginger. Toss in a large bowl with two forks. Whisk vinegar, aminos, and Veganaise together. Add to carrot/ginger mixture. Toss, and then add walnuts and raisins.

Momma told me that her mom always mixed the dressing separately and poured it over the salad. Give it a taste before pouring, and you will be able to tell if it needs salt.

Live long and hear the song of the earth
speak to you through fresh homemade foods.
Life begins in the kitchen.

C.O.W. WOW! SALAD
Carrot Orange Walnut Salad

This is a fantastic splash of flavor and color!

1 lb. carrots, peeled and shredded (about 10)
2 oranges, peeled and cut into bite-sized pieces
½ cup walnuts chopped
2 Tbs cilantro
1 Tbs lemon juice
1 Tbs olive oil

Place the shredded carrots and cut oranges into a bowl and top with walnuts and cilantro. In a separate bowl, whisk olive oil and lemon juice. Add salt and pepper to taste. Pour oil mixture over shredded carrot mixture and gently toss. Serve with joy!

Serving suggestions:

Romaine lettuce leaf boat and hummus topped with c.o.w. salad
Vegetables sautéed in coconut oil and topped with fresh c.o.w. salad
Serves 4.

CRUNCHY CELERY SALAD

6 stalks of celery
1 head of endive (Substitute with 1 cup Napa cabbage or fennel if endive is unavailable.
Both would get that great crunch.)
6 sprigs of parsley
3 large kale leaves, de-stemmed
Sprouts of choice (sunflower seedlings)

Slice and chop ingredients into bite-size pieces, allowing for crunch.
Toss gently together, singing a happy song.

This dressing brings out the best of all your ingredients:

1 Tbs honey	1 Tbs raw apple cider vinegar
1 Tbs olive oil	1 Tbs tamari

Whip dressing ingredients in the food processor until creamy, or use a hand whisk. Whisk away your problems of the day. Then pour dressing on top of your salad, spreading it around in a circle. Toss gently with 2 forks and top with large grain pink Himalayan salt. Serves 4.

Carry courage in your back pocket
and live an exquisite life today!

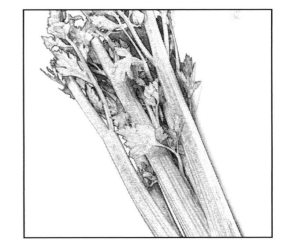

WATERMELON DIVA SALAD

1 5-lb. watermelon
1 red onion
½ cup fresh chopped mint
½ cup fresh chopped parsley
½ cup fresh chopped cilantro
4 Tbs fresh lime juice
salt and pepper

Begin by slicing the onion into thin strips and soaking the slices in cold water for at least an hour. (This removes bitter flavors.) Cut the watermelon into inch-size chunks. In a large bowl, mix the watermelon, mint, cilantro, parsley, lime juice, and onions (drained, with the water discarded). Gently mix before adding salt and pepper to taste. Add salt, gently mix, taste, add more or less.

RED CABBAGE SALAD

½ head of red cabbage, sliced in bite-size pieces
½ fresh lemon
½ tsp Himalayan pink salt
2 tsp apple cider vinegar
2 cloves garlic

Toss the chopped red cabbage with salt and lemon. Let this rest while you process the vinegar and garlic in the food processor. Fold in garlic vinegar mixture and serve fresh, with a smile. :)

If this salad seems too strong for your taste buds, top with some olive oil. Serves 6.

SUMMER TEMPEH SALAD

1 package tempeh
½ cup water
1 Tbs tamari, or real soy sauce
¼ cup finely chopped red onion
½ cup finely chopped red bell pepper
½ cup finely chopped celery
2 Tbs chopped parsley
2 Tbs chopped basil
fresh cracked black pepper

Cut tempeh into bite-size cubes. Place in a frying pan with ½ cup water and tamari. Cover and steam for 10 minutes or till soft, and remove from heat. In a bowl, lightly toss with veggies, herbs and Vegan mayonnaise (page 100). Top with fresh ground pepper and salt to taste. Serve on a bed of lettuce with some grape tomatoes.

CITRUS BEET SALAD

With time, the flavor of this salad grows and marries to create an explosion in your mouth. You can spiralize or use the food processor to shred the beets. You may consider wearing gloves to avoid the red beet stains on your hands.

3-4 cups peeled and spiralized or shredded organic beets
juice of 1 orange
2 Tbs balsamic vinegar
2 Tbs olive oil
1/8 tsp dried oregano
1/8 tsp dried basil
sprinkle of pink Himalayan salt

Mix the dressing ingredients together using a small whisk. Pour over the beets and toss lightly. Serves 6.

When you taste this salad, the sweetness of the orange marries with the balsamic vinegar. They create an instant happiness. The subtle flavor of the herbs makes you think, "WOW!, this is gourmet."

DRESSINGS & TOPPINGS

Dressings

BASIL TAHINI DRESSING

1 cup water
1 cup basil, fresh, washed well
¼ cup tahini

juice of 1 lemon
salt to taste

Wash the basil leaves well and dry with a paper towel, linen, or low-lint cloth. Place basil in food processor or blender and add the tahini, lemon juice, and water. Pulse until smooth. Serves 4.

This vibrant mouth-watering dressing may be used on top of a green leafy salad, zucchini pasta, cooked pasta, or toasted slices of Italian bread topped with cheese and broiled. These little toasts can be made up to two days before and kept in the refrigerator. No one will know after you broil them to perfection and garnish with fresh parsley. If you do not have tahini, you may substitute almond butter, plus the zest of 1 lemon.

VEGAN MAYONNAISE

¼ cup coconut milk
¼ cup coconut oil
1 Tbs olive oil
3 Tbs hemp seeds

½ tsp Himalayan salt
2 Tbs raw apple cider vinegar
smidgen of paprika

Place all ingredients in blender and blend for 5 minutes or until creamy. Taste to make sure there is enough salt for you. Serves 4-6.

CUCUMBER CASHEW SALAD DRESSING

1 cup cucumber, chopped
1 cup cashews, soaked for 48 hours
1 cup filtered water
1 tsp tahini (sesame seed paste)
3 Tbs dulse flakes

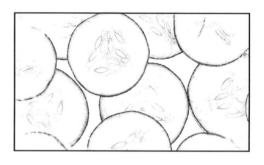

Soak the raw cashews in enough filtered water to cover them, for 48 hours in the refrigerator, rinsing at least once a day. Rinse and drain the nuts and place in a blender or Vitamix. Blend until creamy consistency. (If you blend it well enough, there will be no grittiness from the nuts.) This dressing perks up any salad and is good for your belly and your taste buds.   Serves 4.

If you make a nut-based salad dressing, it becomes a nutrient and protein rich part of your meal.

GOTTA HAVE IT! GARLIC SALAD DRESSING

☆ ☆ ☆ ☆

½ cup olive oil
2 Tbs tamari
2-4 garlic cloves

Peel and chop the garlic, place in food processor. Add oil and tamari, process until creamy. Serves 4 to 8.

TASTY TOASTED ALMOND BUTTER SALAD DRESSING

¼ cup filtered water
3 Tbs balsamic vinegar
2 Tbs roasted or raw almond butter

¼ cup organic olive oil
¼ tsp course ground black pepper
¼ - ½ tsp Himalayan pink salt

Place all ingredients in the food processor. Process until smooth and creamy. Taste and see if you need a kick of cayenne or more salt. The rich oils in this dressing mask the salt, so taste it before you serve it.

TOASTED ALMOND SLIVERS FOR GARNISH AND CRUNCH!

Toast sliced almonds in a dry frying pan over medium heat. Stovetop toasting requires you stay with the project, because the oils in the nuts can burn quickly. Once the nuts start browning, stir them or flip them around the frying pan. As soon as they look done, dump them onto a plate to cool. Otherwise, they will continue to cook and may burn.

Almonds are a health nut's dream come true. This nut delivers nutrients and antioxidants every day, all day. They are loaded with 37 percent of the recommended daily amount of vitamin E in just one ounce.

Almonds have protein and fiber to help balance blood sugar levels. Enjoy them as a topper, as a nut butter and as a nut milk.

One of the most sensual memories I have of New Jersey is driving. Actually, quite a few memories in my life are of driving. I am one of those people who thinks better in open air.

I was riding through the blueberry fields, listening to tapes of my classes, worried about passing an anatomy and physiology exam. I used to be good about over-worrying things; just the thought of that class makes me remember how I gave up my life that entire semester to study and study some more.

But this was a blessing of divine intervention. I inhaled it before I saw it. The aroma overtook me and became an awakening, an overwhelming sense. It was a shift of energy tying me up and spitting me out with a sense of enlightenment. . .a knowing. . .a freedom. Some memories can do that if you let them.

On both sides of the road as far as my eyes could see on the horizon stretched a white misty layer of full billowing blooms of blueberry bushes. I taste this memory every time I make Blueberry Vinaigrette.

BLUEBERRY VINAIGRETTE

½ cup fresh blueberries
1 small clove garlic, chopped
1 tsp white onion
2 Tbs balsamic vinegar
3 drops clear stevia
2-4 Tbs light olive oil

In a blender, whip the berries, garlic, onion, vinegar and stevia until the berries are liquefied. Drizzle the olive oil through the top while all ingredients continue to be whipped. This makes vinaigrette to toss with sliced cucumbers and serve as a side dish. Serves 4.

See also dressings in the section on salads.

Toppers
Make Some! Buy Some!

Toppers are an easy way to add extra flavors, textures and nutrients to any dish. Sometimes I snack on a topper or two just because I can! Use your newfound knowledge about spices, and incorporate what you like and desire to conjure up some tasty toppings. Create an herbal sprinkle that opens your taste buds and fills your senses with flavors. Conscious awareness of our sense of taste and our sense of fullness improves with practice. Take time to tune in to the many toppers and flavors in your kitchen, and you will achieve new culinary delights!

RAW HEMP HEARTS

A super-rich food so far as nutrition is concerned, hemp hearts have a nutty flavor. They contain 30 percent protein, both omega 3 and omega 6 fatty acids, iron and Vitamin E. Hemp seeds are a dense source of plant-based protein that can be whipped into pesto or eaten by the spoonful. Try hemp hearts on top of soup or hot and cold cereals. Blend hemp into a smoothie. Sprinkle hemp seeds on top of your green leafy salad or try some on ice cream. These seeds lose their good qualities when baked, so eat them raw.

HERBAL CHICKPEAS

Drain a can of chickpeas and rinse with water. Sprinkle them with herbs and spices of your choice. One good idea is to use Greek herbs and a dash of cayenne. Top a salad or surprise someone you love with a tray full of these tasty toppers.

MY FAVORITE KALE TOPPER

1 bunch of kale, about 4 cups

Kale Coating:

3 Tbs of Bragg Liquid Aminos
2 tsp chickpea miso
2 Tbs water

Blend kale coating ingredients in food processor. Wash and strip kale from stalks (de-stem). Let dry a bit, and then toss in coating mixture and massage. Oil the dehydrator trays to prevent the kale from sticking. Lay out kale coated with the sauce on dehydrator sheets, with a space between. Dehydrate 3-5 hours or until crisp. Use as a topper on soups or salads and anything else you choose.

KALE TOPPER #2

1 bunch of kale, about 4 cups

Kale Coating:
3 Tbs Tamari
3 Tbs nutritional yeast
2 Tbs water

Blend coating ingredients in a food processor. Wash and strip kale from stalks (de-stem). Let dry a bit, and then toss kale in coating mixture and massage. Oil the dehydrator trays to prevent the kale from sticking. Lay out kale coated with the sauce on dehydrator sheets, with a space between. Deyhdrate 3 to 5 hours or until crisp. Use as a topper, serve as a snack or bag up for travel food.

3 BEANS AND A KALE CRISP TOPPER

I don't know why, but creating this makes me happy. Perhaps this secret joy comes from the fact that I love color, and real food is a vibrant source of many colors.

¼ cup balsamic vinaigrette (pre-made Paul Newman's will do)
1 cup red kidney beans*
1 cup white kidney beans*
1 cup black beans*
¼ cup julienne-sliced, sun-dried tomatoes cut into 1/4" pieces
fresh parsley
salt to taste
3 cups thinly sliced kale
2 Tbs coconut oil
fresh romaine lettuce washed, dried and sliced

*You can use a 15 oz. can of each.

Happily toss the beans and sun-dried tomatoes in the vinaigrette to marinate and marry flavors. The marinade happens without much effort while you are cooking the kale, getting the table set, or overnight, if you plan ahead.

Wash and remove the stems from the kale and slice thin. On the stovetop, heat 2 tablespoons coconut oil to a temperature for frying, so that when you toss in your thinly sliced kale, the oil sears it and crisps the leaves. Searing happens fast, so stand there with your kale, and stir a bit until golden brown. Remove from heat.

Place romaine lettuce on a plate, top with the bean marinade, crispy kale, fresh chopped parsley and sprinkle with course ground Himalayan pink salt! Easy, fancy, and tasty! Serves 4.

SPICY DEHYDRATED ALMOND SLICES

Soak sliced almonds overnight in filtered water in the refrigerator. Rinse in the morning and spread out on dehydrator sheets. Sprinkle with cayenne pepper and Himalayan pink salt. Dehydrate 6-8 hours until almonds are crisp. These spicy toppers are a spark on top of any salad or soup

EASY FAKE BACON

1 cup large flake organic coconut
2 Tbs organic tamari

Toss together. Let rest for 20 minutes. Bake at 400 degrees until crisp and brown, approximately 10-15 minutes.

OMEGA KICK (HEALTHY TOPPER)

1 Tbs nutritional yeast
1 Tbs hemp seeds
1 Tbs chia seeds
1 smidgen cayenne pepper
1 pinch Himalayan pink salt

Mix ingredients together and store in an air-tight jar. Label and use often.

This is a healthy, spicy, cheesy topping you can keep in the fridge and use to perk up almost any dish. Nutritional yeast is cultured with beet molasses. It makes a great cheese substitute, is high in protein, B vitamins, and has a salty flavor with low sodium.

Shoe String Beans

My sneakers were all muddy, So,
Mom put them in the laundry,
And the washer lost the laces,
Which left me in a quandary.
So I sat down in the garden
To think about my plight....
From early dawn until the dusk,
And way into the night.
I know I'd have gold laces
If I were rich as kings and queens;
But I only have a garden.
So I tied them with green beans.

Face Balkum

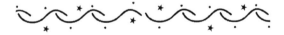

WILTED VEGETABLES

Wilting is a great treatment for driving the flavor into foods!

Wilting green leafy and cruciferous vegetables is a gift from the ancient culinary experts who used salt as a preservative and salt brine to tenderize meat. Salt has the ability to create a process called "osmosis." With a sprinkle of salt, water is dispersed and flavors are driven into the cells of plants, an osmotic action. This is a balancing act that wilts vegetables and adds spice to create a new experience of explosive flavors. Watch out!

The sprinkling of salt on raw vegetables —"the wilt"— tenderizes them, makes them easier to chew and allows for a different texture. Salt helps the marinade enter the vegetables. When you eat this marinated delight, you think, "Yum, spicy flavor." Not "this tastes like green kale or grass." If you take a moment to focus and remember the texture and spice, this becomes a healthy meal that reminds you of how something tasted when Grandma made it!

My memories of family picnics during my childhood always include a sweet cucumber salad. This was made by salting cucumbers and pressing them in a colander or strainer, with a plate to draw out the water, and then seasoning them with sugar water, thinly sliced red onion, and celery seeds. I adapted that recipe and now use wilted cucumbers as a salad topper.

WILTED CUCUMBER SALAD

2 tsp Himalayan pink salt
1 orange
3-4 cucumbers
½ red onion
½ cup honey
¾ cup Bragg Apple Cider Vinegar

Peel the cucumbers leaving some of the skin on them so they look striped. Use a mandolin slicer or a sharp knife to slice the cucumbers very thin. Slice the onion thin (keep separate). Sprinkle salt on top of sliced cucumbers and squeeze orange on top. Toss in a bowl and set aside. Mix honey and vinegar in a measuring cup using a whisk. When the cucumbers are limp and water fills the bowl, pour off water and strain. Add honey vinegar mix and onions. Toss and get ready to eat! Eat as a side salad or a topper.

Honey and vinegar preserve this salad well. It will keep three to five days covered in the refrigerator, so make it ahead of time for a potluck surprise.

WILTED EGGPLANT WITH GREEK SPARKLE

1 firm eggplant (a small eggplant is better because it has fewer seeds)
juice of 1 lemon
½ tsp pink Himalayan salt

Greek seasonings:
¼ tsp dried oregano
¼ tsp dehydrated onion
¼ tsp dehydrated garlic
¼ tsp dried mint

Peel the eggplant and slice into thin strips, about 3" long and 1/8" wide. Place the strips in a bowl and squeeze the lemon juice on top. Sprinkle with salt and herbs, and toss with wooden spoons about every 5 minutes for 20-30 minutes. The eggplant will wilt, absorb the flavors, and transform into a low-cal salad topper or wrap filler. This dish will surprise your guests and shock your family! Serves 4.

ITALIAN WILTED KALE SALAD

1 bunch of kale, de-stemmed
1 lemon
2 tsp Himalayan pink salt
½ cup sun-dried tomatoes julienne-cut or chopped by hand
½ tsp dried oregano
1 Tbs dried basil
fresh cracked black pepper
½ cup fresh parsley

Take the stems out of the kale and slice the leaves very thinly so that they look like angel hair pasta. (These thin veggie strips are called "chiffonade.") Place the kale in a bowl and squeeze the lemon on top. Sprinkle the salt on top and massage lightly. Let rest for 15-20 minutes. Chop the fresh herbs and toss with the sun-dried tomatoes. Turn herbs into wilted kale and toss gently. Serve as a side dish or on top of a green leafy salad with a muffin!
Serves 4.

WILTED RED PEPPERS

4 plump red bell peppers
1 lemon
½ tsp Himalayan pink salt
3 cloves garlic chopped
¼ cup olive oil

Core and slice the peppers into 1/8" strips that are about 3" long. Place in a deep bowl. Squeeze lemon on top and sprinkle with Himalayan pink salt. Toss with forks and let rest for 20 minutes.

Occasionally stir and sing to your peppers, putting good energy in. The peppers will become soft and wilt. Drain the lemon and salt wilt mixture off. Place wilted peppers in a jar with chopped garlic and olive oil to let them marinate. Serve room temperature as a side or a topper. Serves 6.

For whatever reason, red peppers are rarely recognized for the powerhouse status they deserve on any list of nutritional benefits. Antioxidants? Of course. Vitamin C? Great way to cover your daily requirement, and then some. A good source of B6, plus magnesium. Soaring amounts of lycopene, which researchers say helps prevent cancer, especially prostate and lung. And to wrap it all up, there is now research that says, even without the capsaicin that is found in hot peppers, these Red Mamas offer a mild form of thermogenesis that increases your metabolic rate, without that uncomfortable increase in heart rate and blood pressure.

WILTED FENNEL AND APPLE SLICES

2 cups sliced fennel
1 apple
1 lemon
1 tsp Himalayan pink salt

Cut the top off the fennel and remove the outer layers of the fennel bulb. I created this salad to use the outer layers from the bulb because they are tough and hard to chew. Wash and thinly slice the outer layers longways with the grain. Slice the apple into thin slices and toss together. Squeeze the lemon juice on top of the sliced fennel and apple, add salt. Lift and mix the salad about every 10 minutes, let rest to wilt.

Serve as a side dish or a happy topper! Flavors marry and salad becomes savory when eaten the next day.

WILTED BRUSSEL SPROUTS WITH MAPLE SYRUP!

2-3 cups sliced fresh brussel sprouts
1 orange
1 tsp Himalayan pink salt
1 Tbs Maple syrup

Remove some of the outer leaves of the (little cabbages) brussel sprouts to reveal a fresh clean green layer. Cut off the bottom to reveal fresh area, slice and quarter into small thin pieces. Squeeze orange over and sprinkle salt on top. Stir and toss to gently allow juice and salt to coat brussel sprouts. Let wilt activate for about 40 minutes, then top with maple syrup and stir. Enjoy!

Restless Brussel Sprouts

Brussel Sprouts!
Brussel Sprouts!
Everyone shouts for brussel sprouts!
They're little and green,
And look like cabbages.
Cook a lot and eat them like savages!

Face Balkum

SAUERKRAUT

4-5 cups shredded cabbage, loosely packed
1 tsp cumin seeds
1 tsp course ground pepper
2 tsp salt (no minerals, no iodine added)
1-2 cups filtered water (chlorine free)

Shred and chop cabbage into bite-size pieces. You can use a knife or food processor or both. In a large bowl mix, toss, and massage cabbage with spices, salt and water. The mixing process is important. As you mix, the cabbage gathers bacteria from the air to start the fermenting process. Massage the cabbage to release the juices.

Place the cabbage mix in clean glass jars and pack down with the back of a spoon. Leave 1 inch or more of space between the cabbage and the top of the jar. When you press the cabbage down into the jar, make sure the water comes up above the cabbage mixture. Add extra filtered water, if needed. Cover the jars and place in a cool spot. Cabbage ferments best at 72 degrees and usually takes about 3-7 days. Cooler temperatures will take a longer time to ferment; warmer temperatures may spoil the batch. This is the experimental fun of fermenting!

When you eat ferments, which is what foods like sauerkraut are called, start with small amounts. I suggest 1 Tbs. at a meal.

WILTED SPIRALIZED ZUCCHINI

2-4 firm zucchini (6-8 inches long)
juice of 1 lemon
½ tsp salt

Using a spiralizer, with linguine pasta size blade, create zucchini pasta. Squeeze lemon juice on top of zucchini and sprinkle with salt. Using two forks toss the zucchini and turn in the lemon juice and salt. This combination will marinate into the squash and create a lovely lemon flavor to the zucchini.

Serve this as a side dish or on top of quinoa. Keep in the refrigerator for up to 4 days for maximum flavor.

Get bold with this final dish, add your favorite spices and herbs to enhance flavors and create a WOW! Review Spices of the World Chart, page 36.

SWEETS

Sit Up In Your Chair. Sugar Gives You Wrinkles!

An instructor informed a group of women attending a recent seminar that scientists had identified a number of nasty side effects of sugar. They listened with little reaction when they heard sugar causes a raft of negative physical reactions and conditions. What made the audience sit up in their chairs and gasp was the simple truth: "Sugar causes wrinkles."

So I say, make that your anti-sugar mantra! Creating a visual of your face wrinkled up and holding it in your mind for a second may prevent you from reaching for that candy. Or how about this: "I don't need sugar. I am sweet enough!" By the way, don't think sugar is the only thing that causes wrinkles, because that's far from the truth.

Another important fact about sugar is that all sweet foods contain carbohydrates, and all carbohydrates turn to sugar during the digestive process. When you add more sugar to your diet plus eat foods high in carbohydrates, (pasta, dried fruits and fruits in general) you really are on a sugar high and contributing to high blood sugar levels. Carbohydrate calories are used as fuel so we do need them. But really what we need to eat is foods that give us a slow steady energy burn, low in sugar and carbohydrates, and high in nutrients and fiber. How sweet is that?

HAPPY NATURAL SUGAR ALTERNATIVES
Use your judgment, and experiment with moderation and joy.

★ Stevia is a plant that is 200 times sweeter than sugar and contains no calories. Some complain of an aftertaste, but I say, "No calories, sweet taste." Try it. Just remember, all stevia is not created equal. Whole stevia leaf contains stevioside, a proven health benefit. But using certain brands of stevia that have been processed and altered with chemicals and white sugar is not good. The best thing you can do is grow your own plants and harvest them. Dry them and use the leaves. If growing your own stevia plant is not an option, read labels to find the least processed stevia products.

★ Birch sugar Xylitol is a healthy, natural sugar that boosts immunity, heals and repairs, and has anti-aging benefits. It has 40 percent fewer calories than regular white sugar, plus it offers blood sugar balancing benefits and tooth decay fighting properties. Use Xylitol with caution. For some people, it may have a laxative effect. This sweetener may originate from birch bark or corn products; make sure you know its origin.

★ Date sugar is essentially dehydrated dates ground into powder. It can be used as a substitute for brown sugar in any recipe. (Since it is so sweet, use 1/3 less). Date sugar benefits include antioxidants and fiber.

★ Blackstrap molasses contains concentrated minerals, highest in potassium with significant amounts of iron, calcium, magnesium, manganese and copper.

★ Honey, when eaten raw, has more than 5,000 enzymes and antioxidants; is antibacterial; and has been proven to increase athletic performance. Although honey is natural and a good choice, too much of a good thing is still too much.

★ Maple syrup is maple tree sap that is collected and boiled down. During this process, the nutrients remain, making it a sweet, nutrient-rich liquid. Try maple syrup in a summer herb tea. You will be sweetly surprised.

★ Monk fruit, indigenous to China and Thailand, is a green, round melon-looking fruit that is 300 times sweeter than sugar and has fewer calories. Watch out; it is pricey! Experiment with monk fruit in baked goods, smoothies and hot drinks.

★ Coconut sugar is the boiled and dehydrated sap of the coconut palm tree. A tasty light brown sugar, it offers the same number of carbohydrates and calories as table sugar and boasts more nutrients. Coconut sugar's advantage over table sugar is inulin, a type of dietary fiber that feeds the good bacteria (probiotics) in your digestive tract.

ORIGINAL 7 LAYER COOKIES

(This was the recipe before turning into the Heart Healthy version on the next page. No mixer required.) It is included to show you how easy it is to substitute healthy choices in almost any recipe.

1 stick butter
1 cup graham cracker crumbs
1 cup shredded coconut
1 ½ cups chopped nuts
1 cup chocolate bits
1 cup butterscotch or peanut-butter bits
1 can sweetened condensed milk

Preheat your oven to 350 degrees. Melt the butter and then pour into a 9x13" pan; be sure that it coats the bottom evenly. Sprinkle these over the butter in order: graham cracker crumbs, shredded coconut, nuts, chocolate bits and butterscotch or peanut-butter bits. Drizzle the can of condensed milk over entire mixture. Bake for 30 min. Let it cool in the pan, and then cut it into squares. Makes 15 squares.

HEART CENTERED 7 LAYER COOKIES
(No Mixer Required)

¼ cup coconut oil
2 cups pecans
½ cup chia flour (ground chia seeds)
1 cup shredded coconut
1 cup sliced almonds
1 cup vegan chocolate chips
½ cup almond butter
1 can coconut milk (the thick one found in the Thai food section)
Top with organic, fancy grade coconut flakes.

The first organ to develop, the heart is the seat of all emotional thought. The heart is the home of the vital force, home to the spirit.

Preheat your oven to 350 degrees and while it's warming, melt the coconut oil in a 9x13" pan. Process the pecans in a food processor until ground to flour consistency, then mix with the chia flour and sprinkle into the pan. The sprinkled flours act as a mock graham cracker crust and are much healthier.

Sprinkle these ingredients over the flour base in this order: shredded coconut, sliced almonds, vegan chocolate chips and coconut milk. Drizzle or dollop the almond butter on, then top with fancy grade coconut flakes to add a decorative touch. They brown up beautifully! Bake 30 min. Cool and cut into squares. You can make it, cool it, cover it and store in the refrigerator for up to 1 week. Pull it out, cut up and serve! Serves 15 healthy heart-centered treats.

Everybody loves this recipe, and it is packed with good stuff! To make it a bit healthier, I put a layer of spirulina and ¼ cup soaked goji berries on before the almond butter, and it looks like a Christmas treat.

BLACK BEAN BROWNIE BITES

1 15-oz. can black beans, rinsed and drained
¼ cup cocoa powder
¼ cup almond flour
1 dash cayenne
¼ tsp salt
½ tsp baking powder
¼ cup chia gel (1 Tbs +1 tsp ground chia
      flour in 1 cup warm water. Let rest
      to congeal and make a gel.)
¼ cup almond butter
¼ cup xylitol
½ tsp vanilla
½ cup dairy-free mini chocolate chips
mini muffin tin
mini muffin cupcake liners

Preheat your oven to 350 degrees. Then make the chia gel and set aside to set up. In the food processor, process the dry ingredients (except the mini-chocolate chips) to evenly distribute them. Add the wet ingredients to the food processor and cream the mixture, processing for about 3 minutes. Turn out the mixture into a bowl and fold in the mini chips. (These chips look great dropped on top of the bites as well.) Cook at 350 degrees for 15 -25 minutes. Let cool before serving. I call these brownie bites because they are bite size and they remind me of a decadent brownie without the wheat and butter!

CHIA ENERGY CHEW

½ cup chia flour (ground chia seeds)
¼ cup chia seeds
½ tsp Himalayan salt
1 cup chopped dates
½ cup honey
2 cups pecans - 1 cup chopped by hand, 1 cup processed

Put 1 cup of pecans in a food processor & whip until fine. Chop the other cup of pecans by hand and set aside. When pecans are finely ground, add chia flour, chia seeds, salt and dates. Blend the mixture 1-2 minutes until completely mixed. Add honey and process until the mixture holds together. Remove the mixture from food processor and place in a large bowl. Hand mix in the hand-chopped pecans. Scoop out bite-size chia chews and roll in your hands or pat together. Serve and enjoy!

COCONUT CHIA PUDDING

1 Tbs chia flour (ground chia seeds)
¾ cup coconut milk
1 Tbs unsweetened coconut flakes
A few soaked goji berries on top

Chia flour is easily made by grinding the seeds in a blender or coffee grinder. Soak your goji berries in warm water, and they will hydrate faster, or soak overnight in the refrigerator. Mix chia flour into coconut milk, add coconut flakes and let rest until the mixture firms. Top with a few goji berries and enjoy. WOW! That was easy!

If you desire it sweeter, add some stevia. It won't spike your sugar levels and it has no calories! You may also consider swapping out coconut milk for almond milk and adding almonds, cashew milk and cashews. Or you might go wild with carrot juice, ginger and chia seeds.

SUPER FOOD FAIRY CRUNCHY PUDDING

Crunchy pudding was born when a guest (I once was an innkeeper.) told me his story about how his wife got him to eat a healthy yogurt, topped with granola for breakfast. Being just a little silly and quite creative, he made up the title, and I share his enthusiasm with you. It is interesting how a title and ingredient change can create a nutritious joyful meal.

2 Tbs chia flour (grind up those chia seeds in the blender)
1 cup unsweetened coconut milk (or vegan milk of choice)
4 drops lemon-flavored stevia (or flavored stevia of choice)

Super food toppings:
1 Tbs hemp seeds
1 Tbs happy snacks

Mix chia flour into milk and let sit about 10 minutes. Chia will set up faster if the milk is warm, so give it a few minutes, or make it the night before and let it set up in the refrigerator. Add your sweetener and super food toppings. Serves 2.

CHOCOHOLIC* KALE COOKIES

1 cup almond flour
1 cup gluten-free flour, rice blend, found in most grocery stores near the cake mixes
½ cup quinoa flakes
1 cup dark cocoa powder
1½ tsp salt
1 tsp baking soda
1 tsp baking powder
dash cayenne
½ cup birch sugar xylitol
1 cup organic powdered sugar
½ cup coconut oil
1 cup almond milk
1 cup shredded kale
½ cup Vegan chocolate chips
(optional 1 cup chocolate chips, for chocoholics out there)

Preheat your oven to 375 degrees. In a large bowl, mix the gluten-free flours together with the other dry ingredients. Place the sugars, coconut oil and almond milk in food processor and cream. Then add the wet ingredients to the dry mixture. Gently fold in the shredded kale and vegan chocolate chips. Take small balls of dough, roll in your hands and press to form tablespoon-sized cookies. Then flatten to create a cookie shape. Bake cookies for 10-12 minutes until slightly brown on bottom.

*Chocoholic - a person who is extremely fond of chocolate!

CHOCOLATE SPICE COOKIES
Refrigerate overnight or these spices will burn your tongue!

¾ cup non-dairy butter substitute, Earth Balance or non-hydrogenated vegetable
    shortening
½ cup organic sugar
½ cup powdered sugar
¼ cup molasses
2¼ cups flour (wheat or gluten-free blend)
1/3 cup cocoa powder
2 tsp baking soda
1 Tbs ground ginger
1 tsp Himalayan salt
2 tsp cinnamon
2 tsp ground cloves
dash cayenne pepper
¼ cup chia gel

Gluten-free Blend:
    1 cup white rice flour
    1 cup sorghum flour
    1 cup tapioca flour
    1 cup cornstarch
    1 cup almond flour

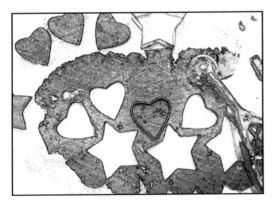

Using a mixer, cream together butter and organic sugar. Add chia gel and molasses. Whip until creamy. In another bowl, combine and mix together dry ingredients by using a wire whisk so spices are evenly distributed. Add half a cup of dry ingredients to wet mixture and cream together. Add more dry mixture until done. Best if stored overnight in the refrigerator. Scoop out bite-size cookie treats or get out that rolling pin and have some fun. Place on a cookie sheet lined with parchment paper or sprayed with coconut oil. Bake 375° for 8-10 minutes. When you create cookies without eggs, cooking them can be a bit tricky. They can dry out quickly; don't overbake. This is a great cookie dough to freeze and pull out on a cold winter's day. Why not surprise someone you love?

COCAO COCONUT LOVE DROPS

1½ cups raw pecans
¾ cup chia flour (ground chia seeds)
3 Tbs raw cacao powder
pinch of salt
dash of cayenne
½ cup finely chopped dates
¼ cup maple syrup
¼ cup organic coconut oil
½ cup dried coconut flakes, reserved for
coating the love drop at the end

Using a 6-cup food processor, process the pecans, grinding them to a flour-like consistency. Pour into the food processor the chia flour, cacao powder, salt, and cayenne. Process these together until dry ingredients are evenly distributed. Add the finely chopped dates, coconut oil and maple syrup. Process until the mixture melds together. (When it holds together and falls off the sides of the processor, it is melded.) Scoop the cocoa dough with a teaspoon and drop into the dried coconut flakes. Gently roll to coat the cocoa dough in shredded coconut and serve up the love! Yields 35-38 melt in your mouth, scrumptious love drops.

MELT IN YOUR MOUTH COCONUT SHORTBREAD COOKIE
(WITH GOJI AND CHOCOLATE!)

This cookie was inspired by my love of shortbread and hot tea. It is worth the trip to the health food store for these ingredients!

½ cup goji berries
boiling water
1 tsp salt
1 tsp baking soda
1 cup dairy-free mini chocolate chips
1¾ cup coconut flour
½ cup coconut flakes
1 cup non-hydrogenated vegetable shortening
½ cup birch sugar (xylitol)
½ cup organic confectionery sugar
2 ½ Tbs gojiwater left from soaking goji berries

Preheat your oven to 400 degrees. Place the goji berries in a small bowl or glass cup and almost cover with boiling water. The nutritional value of goji berries is more readily absorbed when they are hydrated. Measure and mix all the dry ingredients in a separate bowl to evenly distribute them. Drain the water from the goji berries and save. In a food processor, cream the shortening, the sugars, and the warm goji water. Add the hydrated goji berries to dry mixture, and toss them around a bit. Turn and fold the wet mixture into the dry ingredients using a spatula. Then mix by hand. This saves time and puts your good energy and love into these cookies. Taking your time to fold the ingredients together, think of three things you are grateful for, such as, "I am so grateful I don't have to make chocolate chips. I just create good stuff with them." Using a scoop or spoon, scoop out and press the dough together to create teaspoon-sized cookies, and place on unbleached parchment paper. Bake 10 minutes.

PUMPKIN MINI MUFFIN OR COOKIE! A MOOKIE

This recipe creates a treat that tastes best when the dough is refrigerated overnight before baking.

1 15-oz. can of organic pumpkin (not pumpkin pie filling)
¾ cup coconut oil
1 cup xylitol (birch sugar)
1½ tsp vanilla
2½ cups gluten-free flour
1½ tsp baking soda
1 tsp Himalayan salt
1½ tsp cinnamon
½ tsp nutmeg
¼ cup chia seeds
1 cup raisins
1½ cups chopped walnuts

Cream the pumpkin, coconut oil, xylitol and vanilla together in a large bowl. In another bowl, combine all of the dry ingredients. Mix together to evenly distribute spices, salt, and soda among the flour. Take about a ½ cup of the flour mixture out, and toss the nuts and raisins in to coat them with flour. This prevents them from sticking together. Add the dry mixture to creamed pumpkin mixture, ½ cup at a time. Stir in the flour-coated nuts and raisins. Refrigerate the dough overnight. The following morning preheat your oven to 350 degrees. Scoop out dough into coconut-oiled mini-muffin cups or scoop out small bite-sized cookies onto parchment paper and bake for 10–12 minutes. You can split this recipe and freeze half to pull out and surprise someone another time! Makes 3 dozen mookies or mini muffins.

ORANGE GOJI SURPRISE!

¾ cup chia gel
3 Tbs fresh orange peel
4 Tbs fresh orange juice
1 tsp vanilla
1 cup coconut oil
1/3 cup molasses
½ cup organic sugar
¾ cup goji berries soaked (drained, drink the juice)
½ cup lucuma powder
1 cup millet sprouted grains
1 cup amaranth
1 ½ cup quinoa
1 tsp salt
1 cup chocolate chips
1 ½ tsp guar gum
2 Tbs baking powder

Place chia gel, orange peel, fresh orange juice, vanilla, coconut oil, molasses, and sugar in food processor and whip until well mixed. In another bowl, mix dry ingredients with a whisk until evenly distributed. Add wet mixture to dry, folding in and stirring. Last, gently stir in goji berries. Cookie batter will be dense, firm, and may look a bit grainy. Let sit while you preheat the oven to 375 degrees. Scoop out teaspoon-size cookies (I use a scoop.) Bake at 375 degrees for 12 minutes.

RAW PUMPKIN PIE

2 cups raw pumpkin, chopped small
1 cup almond butter
3 Tbs fresh lemon juice
4 Tbs raw honey
½ tsp nutmeg
½ tsp ground dry ginger
¼ tsp Himalayan pink salt

In a blender or food processor, combine all ingredients until smooth. The consistency should be that of pancake batter. Pour into prepared piecrust and chill overnight. Raw pie crust recipe below.

If you are not into the calories of the pie crust, this makes a fabulous pudding that becomes even tastier if you sprinkle nuts on top.

RAW PIE CRUST

1 cup pecans
1 cup walnuts
1 cup almonds
1 cup pitted chopped dates

In the food processor, grind the nuts into a graham-cracker-like meal. Add the dates and process to evenly distribute all ingredients. Coat a pie dish with coconut oil. Place nut meal in dish and press flat with a spoon to create the pie crust. Pour pie filling in and let rest in the refrigerator overnight. Serve as a sweet side to a meal or as a surprise dessert! Serves 8

WHEAT-FREE OATMEAL COOKIE

1 cup oat flour (easily made by putting oatmeal in the food processor)
½ cup gluten-free flour mix
1 tsp baking soda
1 tsp cinnamon
dash cayenne
1 tsp salt
3 cups oatmeal
½ cup organic raisins
½ cup dried cranberries
1/3 cup vegan butter (Earth Balance), softened
¾ cup organic brown sugar
½ cup organic sugar
½ cup chia gel

Chia gel is ground chia (chia flour) 1 tablespoon to 1 cup warm water. This makes the perfect egg substitute. ¼ cup equals 1 egg.

Place all dry ingredients in a mixing bowl and stir to evenly distribute the spices. Use about ¼ cup of this flour mixture to coat the raisins and cranberries. This will prevent them from sticking together. Mix room temperature butter, sugars, and chia gel in food processor or whip together with mixer. Add wet to dry, then fold in dried fruit. Refrigerate batter overnight to create the best plump cookie. Bake at 375° 10-12 minutes. Makes 3 dozen cookies.

SPICY CHIA BROWNIE

¼ cup + 1 Tbs cocao powder
1 cup chia flour (ground chia seeds)
¼ cup chia seeds
¼ cup shredded coconut
½ tsp salt
½ tsp ginger
pinch of cayenne
½ cup chopped dates
¼ cup + 1 Tbs honey

Place dry ingredients in food processor and mix to evenly distribute them. Add dates and honey. Then process until a ball forms. Press into a 5"x 7" glass dish and refrigerate. Three batches of this will make a 9"x 13" dish.

According to the Aztecs, the god Quetzalcoatl descended from heaven on a beam of the morning star, bringing with him a coca tree stolen from paradise. Both they and the Mayan culture used cocoa to brew a thick unsweetened beverage they drank cold as a health elixier. They called it "xocoatl." Since they had no knowledge of sugar, they chose various spices, such as cinnamon, or the musk of hot chili peppers to add flavor.

GLUTEN-FREE PEANUT BUTTER COOKIE SURPRISE

½ cup gluten-free flour (Bobs Red Mill)
½ cup rice flour
½ cup almond flour
Smidgen of cayenne
1 tsp pink Himalayan salt
1 Tbs baking soda
2 tsp baking powder
½ cup non-hydrogenated vegetable shortening
1 cup chunky peanut butter
1 cup 10x powdered sugar
½ cup date sugar
¼ cup chia gel
(¼ cup warm water with 2 teaspoons chia flour hydrates to make an egg substitute)
1 cup mini vegan chocolate chips

Preheat oven to 350 degrees, 325 degrees convection bake.

Sift the dry ingredients together in a separate bowl. Using an electric mixer or food processor whip together the shortening, peanut butter, sugars, and chia gel. Add dry ingredients a half cup at a time and mix well. Turn in chocolate chips or save to sprinkle on top.

In your hand, roll a teaspoon-size dough ball, place it on an oiled cookie sheet and press down with a fork. Bake 8-10 minutes.

VEGAN, GLUTEN-FREE, DELIGHTFULLY DELICIOUS, AND SPICY HERMIT COOKIES

¼ cup tapioca flour
¼ cup gluten-free flour
1 cup almond flour
2 tsp ground cinnamon
1 tsp baking powder
2 tsp baking soda
1 tsp ground ginger
½ tsp ground nutmeg
1 tsp salt
¼ tsp ground cloves

1 smidgen cayenne pepper
½ cup brown sugar - packed
½ cup non-hydrogenated vegetable shortening
¼ cup dark molasses
¼ cup chia gel
1 cup chopped dates
½ cup sliced almonds
½ cup fancy large flake coconut
¼ cup more tapioca flour

In a medium bowl, mix the dry ingredients together with a whisk to evenly distribute the spices. Set aside. In a small bowl, mix nuts, dried fruits and ¼ cup tapioca flour. This will coat and separate the dried fruits and nuts and help to keep them separate within in the cookie.

Make the chia gel, egg substitute: Chia flour and hot water, 1 Tbs chia flour to 1 cup hot water, Let set until it gels, about 5 minutes. Place sugar, shortening, and molasses in food processor. Add chia gel and process till creamy.

Add flour mixture half at a time to creamed mixture in food processor to mix well. You can use a mixer for all of this as well. Place coated nuts and dried fruit in medium bowl and add wet cookie dough. Fold together with a spatula until mixture shows no white flour. Cover and refrigerate for 4 hours or overnight. This gives the spices time to marry. Dollop teaspoon-size cookies out on a parchment-covered cookie sheet.

Cook 350 degrees for 10-12 minutes.   Makes 2 dozen spicy hermits!

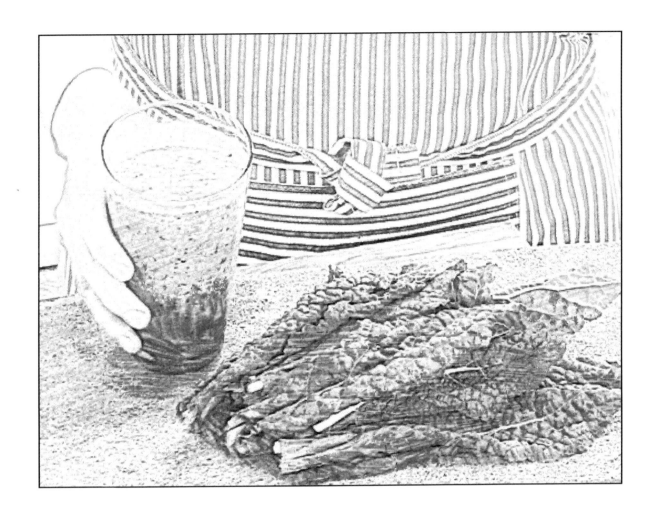

SMOOTHIES

DANCING SMOOTHIES

1 cup nut or seed milk
1 Tbs super food of choice
¼ cup raw, soaked nuts or seeds (minimum 6 hours)
½ avocado
¼ to 1 cup of water

Choose one of the following leafy greens: 3 cups spinach, 2 large kale leaves, or 2 handfuls salad greens. Pick and choose, experiment with your ingredients. Blend the leafy greens with the above ingredients to preferred consistency.

TRY A SMOOTHIE A DAY!

SUNDAY HEART-CENTERED SMOOTHIE!

1 cup almond milk
1 cup frozen peaches
2 cups spinach or kale leaves
1 cup ice
¼ tsp cinnamon
¼ tsp nutmeg
pinch of cayenne
pinch of Himalayan pink salt

Place all ingredients in a blender and whip up with joy. Be careful to add and taste the amount of cayenne consciously! Serves 1-3.

MONDAY, BRAIN BUILDER WITH SPICE!

2 Tbs walnuts
2 Tbs goji berries
2 Tbs chia seeds or flour
1 cup almond milk
1 Tbs cocoa
dash of cayenne
pinch of Himalayan pink salt
add more liquid to preferred consistency

Soak walnuts and goji berries in ¼ cup water overnight in refrigerator. Place almond milk in blender with all ingredients and whip. Be careful to add, and taste the amount of cayenne. Serves 1.

TUESDAY, IMMUNE BOOST SMOOTHIE!

2 cups plain coconut milk
1 cup blueberries
2 Tbs hemp seeds
2 cups spinach
1 cup ice cubes
pinch of Himalayan pink salt
Stevia to taste

Place the coconut milk and other ingredients in blender or Vitamix and whip to perfection. Serves 1-2.

SWEETS

WEDNESDAY, LUNG HEALTH SMOOTHIE!

2 cups apple juice (fresh is best)
2 Tbs chia seeds
1 Tbs Diatomaceous earth
pinch of Himalayan pink salt
1 cup ice cubes

Blend or shake in a glass jar! Serves 1-2 .

THURSDAY, SOOTHING DIGESTIVE SMOOTHIE!

1 cup fresh pineapple
1 cup coconut milk
¼ tsp ground ginger
2 Tbs hemp seeds
pinch of Himalayan pink salt

Place the coconut milk, pineapple, and other ingredients in blender or Vitamix
and whip to perfection. Serves1-2.

FRIDAY, KIDNEY HEALTH SMOOTHIE!

1 cup frozen or fresh banana
2 cups coconut or almond milk
2 Tbs chia seeds
1 tsp Blackstrap molasses
½ tsp cinnamon
pinch of Himalayan pink salt

Place the coconut milk, banana and other ingredients in blender or Vitamix and whip to perfection. Serves 1-2.

SATURDAY, DETOX SMOOTHIE!

2 cups almond milk
2 Tbs pumpkin seeds (raw and soaked)
2 cups kale leaves
2 Tbs hemp seeds
1 Tbs Diatomaceous earth
pinch of Himalayan pink salt

Place ingredients in blender or Vitamix and whip to perfection. Serves 1-2

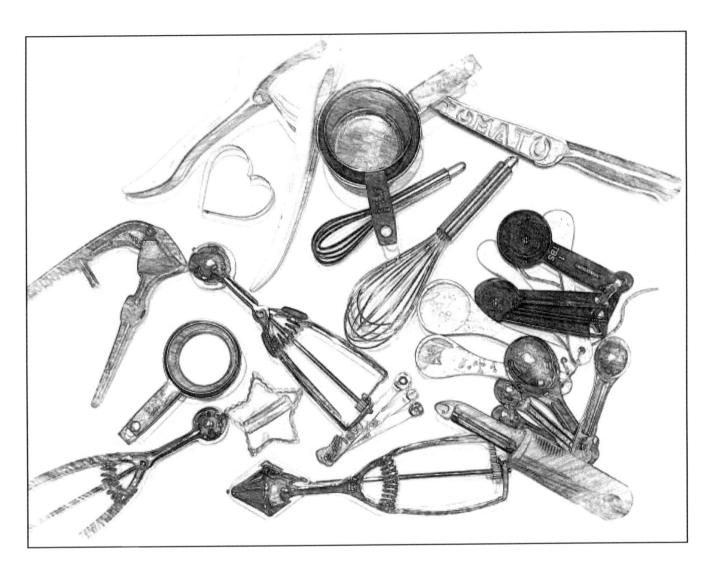

GLOSSARY

Terms

Black pepper coarse ground: found in supermarket near other fine ground pepper

Bragg Aminos: non-fermented soy sauce substitute

Dehydrator: tool used to preserve foods; sheets are for drying wet batter, trays for vegetables and other larger items

Cayenne pepper: red powder from red chili peppers

Chia seeds: black or white seeds, an energy booster, high in healthy fats

Chia flour: ground chia seeds, used to create egg substitutes

Dulse: red algae, high nutrients

Filtered water: water with chlorine, bacteria, heavy metal sand toxins filtered out

Hemp seeds or hemp hearts: balanced protein, most nutritious seed in the world

Hing - asofoeta, devil's dung: used as a flavor similar to leeks

Large flake coconut: large flakes to create more texture and flavors

Miso: fermented soybean or grain seasoning

Nutritional yeast: deactivated yeast grown on molasses

Raw nuts, uncooked nuts, or dehydrated under 125°

Soy sauce: also called "soya"; brewed from fermented wheat, soybeans and salt

Spiralizer: tool used to cut vegetables into thin long pasta shapes

Tahini: sesame seed paste

Tamari: darker, richer, deep-flavored soy sauce

Toppers: healthy toppings to boost flavor and nutrients

Vegan Shopping List
Choose Organic, Fresh and Raw When Possible
Reach for quality ingredients, no sugar, no chemical preservatives

Produce
- ☐ Avocado
- ☐ Broccoli
- ☐ Celery
- ☐ Carrots
- ☐ Cabbage
- ☐ Cucumber
- ☐ Green / String Beans
- ☐ Green Leafy Vegetables (kale, chard, spinach, lettuce, collard greens, beet greens, dandelion leafs, etc.)
- ☐ Seasonal Vegetables (pumpkin, endive, fennel, kohlrabi, etc.)
- ☐ Tomatoes
- ☐ Mushrooms (shiitake, portobello, etc.)

Fruit
- ☐ Apples
- ☐ Bananas
- ☐ Lemons
- ☐ Seasonal Fruits (strawberries, tangerines, pears, cherries, oranges, etc.)

Nuts & Seeds
- ☐ Almonds
- ☐ Almond Butter
- ☐ Brazil Nuts
- ☐ Cashews
- ☐ Flax Seeds
- ☐ Hemp Seeds
- ☐ Pine Nuts
- ☐ Pumpkin Seeds
- ☐ Sesame Seeds
- ☐ Sunflower Seeds

COOKING UP HEALTH, WELLNESS & JOY !

Oils
- ☐ Extra Virgin Coconut Oil
- ☐ Extra Virgin Olive Oil
- ☐ Sesame Oil
- ☐ Pumpkinseed Oil

Sweeteners
- ☐ Raw Organic Honey
- ☐ Liquid Stevia
- ☐ 100% Pure Maple Syrup

Grains & Pasta
- ☐ Almond Flour
- ☐ Rice Flour
- ☐ Coconut Flour
- ☐ Chickpea Flour
- ☐ Buckwheat Flour
- ☐ Gluten-Free Flour Blends
- ☐ Rice Pasta
- ☐ Quinoa
- ☐ Teff

Superfoods
- ☐ Carob Powder
- ☐ Cacao Powder (or nibs)
- ☐ Goji Berries
- ☐ Green or Wheatgrass Powder
- ☐ Lucuma Powder
- ☐ Maca Powder

Herbs
- ☐ Garlic
- ☐ Ginger
- ☐ Onions
- ☐ Fresh Herbs (parsley, basil, etc.)

Spices / Salt
- ☐ Himalayan Pink Salt
- ☐ Cayenne
- ☐ Raw Vanilla Beans (or powder)
- ☐ Cinnamon
- ☐ Herbs of Choice (dried or fresh)

Condiments
- ☐ Pesto
- ☐ Tapenade - Black Olives
- ☐ Tapenade - Sun-dried Tomatoes
- ☐ Black Olives
- ☐ Salsa
- ☐ Artichoke Dip
- ☐ Stone Ground Mustard (homemade)
- ☐ Apple Cider Vinegar
- ☐ Tamari (soy)
- ☐ Miso (unpasturized) - chickpea
- ☐ Raw Sauerkraut
- ☐ Tahini
- ☐ Liquid Aminos, Bragg, Coconut

References

Batmangheliddj, F. (2003) Water for Health, for Healing, for Life: You're Not Sick You're Thirsty. New York New, York: Warner Books.

Bragg, P. (1989). Apple Cider Vinegar Health System. Santa Barbara, California: Health Science.

Boutenko, V. (2007). 12 Steps to Raw Foods, How to End Your Dependency on Cooked Foods. Berkley, California: North Atlantic Books.

Cousens, G. (2000). Conscious Eating. Berkley, California: North Atlantic Books.

Gross, T. (1996). The Last Word on Power. New York, New York: Double Day.

Brotman, J. (1999). Raw the Uncookbook. New York, New York: Harper Collins Publishing.

Kenton, L. S. (1985). Raw Energy. New York, New York: Warner Books.

Lepore, D. (1985). The Ultimate Healing System. Woodland Publishing Inc. Don Lepore.

Pitchford, P. (2002). Healing with Whole Foods. Berkeley, California: North Atlantic Books.

Murphy, R. (2006). Nature's Materia Medica. Third edition Lotus Health Institute.

Meyerowitz, S. (1996). Juice Fasting and Detoxification. Great Barrington, Massachusetts: The Sprout House.

Toscano, J. (2009). Delicious Delites - the Balance of Life. Morris Press Cookbooks.

Wigmore, A. Living Foods Life Style Handbook. Rincon, PR: Ann Wigmore Natural Health Institute.

Wolfe, D. (2009). Super Foods: The Food and Medicine of the Future. Berkeley, California: North Atlantic Books.

This is what you shall do; Love the earth and sun and the animals, despise riches, give alms to every one that asks, stand up for the stupid and crazy, devote your income and labor to others, hate tyrants, argue not concerning God, have patience and indulgence toward the people, take off your hat to nothing known or unknown or to any man or number of men, go freely with powerful uneducated persons and with the young and with the mothers of families, read these leaves in the open air every season of every year of your life, re-examine all you have been told at school or church or in any book, dismiss whatever insults your own soul, and your very flesh shall be a great poem and have the richest fluency not only in its words but in the silent lines of its lips and face and between the lashes of your eyes and in every motion and joint of your body.

Walt Whitman

ABOUT THE AUTHOR

Judith M. Toscano, ND, is a health professional with an extensive and diverse background. Known to her friends, colleagues and clients as "Jude," she uses knowledge, experience and joyful cooking classes to motivate and empower people to create their own realistic and healthy lifestyle. As one patient explained: "Along with her extensive knowledge about natural remedies, homeopathy and her 'woman's intuition,' she has helped me with food choices, natural health protocols and lifestyle changes that create a road toward better health for me that is easy and realistic."

Having earned a bachelor's degree in fine art, as well as a teaching certificate, after graduation Jude turned her attention to the health sciences. She holds a degree in natural medicine, and certifications in a wide variety of specialities, including naturopathy, occupational therapy, massage and colon hydrotherapy. Her certifications in the field of nutrition include green live food cuisine, conscious eating and expanding culinary joy. Finally, she has studied Qijong and maintains a lively interest in the medical practices of cultures throughout the world.

This is her second cookbook. The first, published in 2007 and entitled *Delicious Delites -- The Balance of Life*, incorporates her journey to raw food science and treasured family recipes.

Acknowledgments and Gratitude

Special thanks go out to everyone who helped me along this writing journey. I so appreciate the many smiles I received. Because of each of you, it has been, in the words of the always wonderful Shel Silverstein, "a hug o war" instead of a tug of war.

And, as he concludes, everyone grins and everyone wins!

Made in the USA
San Bernardino, CA
03 June 2017